THE THEORY
OF
ALGEBRAIC NUMBERS

By
HARRY POLLARD
Associate Professor of Mathematics
Cornell University

THE
CARUS MATHEMATICAL MONOGRAPHS

Published by

THE MATHEMATICAL ASSOCIATION OF AMERICA

———

Editorial Committee

THE CARUS MATHEMATICAL MONOGRAPHS are an expression of the desire of Mrs. Mary Hegeler Carus, and of her son, Dr. Edward H. Carus, to contribute to the dissemination of mathematical knowledge by making accessible at nominal cost a series of expository presentations of the best thoughts and keenest researches in pure and applied mathematics. The publication of the first four of these monographs was made possible by a notable gift to the Mathematical Association of America by Mrs. Carus as sole trustee of the Edward C. Hegeler Trust Fund. The sales from these have resulted in the Carus Monograph Fund, and the Mathematical Association has used this as a revolving book fund to publish the succeeding monographs.

The expositions of mathematical subjects which the monographs contain are set forth in a manner comprehensible not only to teachers and students specializing in mathematics, but also to scientific workers in other fields, and especially to the wide circle of thoughtful people who, having a moderate acquaintance with elementary mathematics, wish to extend their knowledge without prolonged and critical study of the mathematical journals and treatises. The scope of this series includes also historical and biographical monographs.

The following monographs have been published:

The Carus Mathematical Monographs

NUMBER NINE

THE THEORY
OF
ALGEBRAIC NUMBERS

By

HARRY POLLARD
Cornell University

Published by

THE MATHEMATICAL ASSOCIATION OF AMERICA

Distributed by

JOHN WILEY AND SONS, INC.

To H. M. P.

PREFACE

The purpose of this monograph is to make available in English the elementary parts of classical algebraic number theory. An earlier version in mimeographed form was used at Cornell University in the spring term of 1947–48, and the present version has accordingly profited from the criticisms of several readers. I am particularly indebted to Miss Leila R. Raines for her painstaking assistance in the revision and preparation of the manuscript for publication.

HARRY POLLARD

CONTENTS

CHAPTER I

DIVISIBILITY

1. **Uniqueness of factorization.** Elementary number theory has for its object the study of the integers 0, ± 1, ± 2, $\cdots$. Certain of these, the *prime* numbers, occupy a special position; they are the numbers m which are different from 0 and ± 1, and which possess no factors other than ± 1 and $\pm m$. For example $2, 3, -5$ are prime, whereas $6 = 2 \cdot 3$, $9 = 3^2$ are not. The importance of the primes is due to the fact that, together with 0 and ± 1, all the other integers can be constructed from them. The fundamental theorem of arithmetic asserts that *every integer greater than 1 can be factored in one and only one way, apart from order, as the product of positive prime numbers.* Thus

$$12 = 2^2 \cdot 3 = 2 \cdot 3 \cdot 2 = 3 \cdot 2^2$$

are the only factorizations of 12 into positive prime factors, and these factorizations all yield precisely the same factors; the only difference among them is in the order of appearance of the factors.

We shall give a proof of the fundamental theorem of arithmetic. In the course of it the following fact will play a decisive role: every collection, finite or infinite, of non-negative integers contains a smallest one. The validity of this assumption will not be debated here; it is certainly clear intuitively, and the reader may take it to be one of the defining properties of integers. Some preliminary theorems will be established first.

THEOREM 1.1. *If a and b are integers, $b > 0$, then there exist integers q and r such that*

$$a = bq + r,$$

where $0 \leq r < b$. The integers q and r are unique.

Consider the rational number $\frac{a}{b}$ and let q be the largest integer which does not exceed it. Then $q \leq \frac{a}{b}$, but $q + 1 > \frac{a}{b}$. Define r as $a - bq$. Since $\frac{r}{b} = \frac{a}{b} - q \geq 0$, and $b > 0$, it follows that $r \geq 0$. Also from $1 > \frac{a}{b} - q = \frac{a - bq}{b} = \frac{r}{b}$ we conclude that $r < b$.

To show that q and r are unique suppose that q' and r' is any pair of integers for which

$$a = bq' + r', \qquad 0 \leq r' < b.$$

If $q' > q$, then $q' \geq q + 1$, so that

$$r' = a - bq' \leq a - b(q + 1) = r - b < 0;$$

this contradicts $r' \geq 0$. If $q' < q$, then $q \leq q - 1$, so that

$$r' = q - bq' \geq a - b(q - 1) = r + b \geq b;$$

this contradicts $r' < b$.

Then both possibilities $q' > q$, $q' < q$ are ruled out. It follows that $q' = q$, and hence that $r' = r$. This completes the proof of Theorem 1.1.

We shall say that two integers a and b are *relatively prime* if they share no factors except ± 1. Thus 5 and 9 are relatively prime, whereas 6 and 9 are not.

THEOREM 1.2. *If a and b are relatively prime then there exist integers s and t for which $as + bt = 1$.*

Observe that there is no assertion about the uniqueness of s and t. In fact if $a = 3$, $b = 5$ we have

$$2 \cdot 3 - 1 \cdot 5 = 1, \qquad -3 \cdot 3 + 2 \cdot 5 = 1.$$

To prove the theorem note first that neither a nor b can be zero. Consider the set of all numbers of the form

$ax + by$, where x and y are integers. If we choose $x = 1$, $y = 0$, and then $x = -1$, $y = 0$, it is clear that a and $-a$ are both in the set. Since $a \neq 0$, one of a and $-a$ is positive, so the set contains some positive numbers. Let d be the smallest positive number in the set, and write $d = as + bt$.

By Theorem 1.1 we can find q and r so that

$$b = dq + r, \qquad 0 \leq r < d.$$

Then

$$r = b - dq = b - (as + bt)q = a(-sq) + b(1 - qt),$$

so that r is also in the set. Now $0 < r < d$ is not possible, since d is the *least* positive number in the set. The only alternative is $r = 0$. Hence $b = dq$. A similar argument, beginning with

$$a = dq' + r', \qquad 0 \leq r' < d$$

shows that $r' = 0$, $a = dq'$.

This proves that d is a factor shared by both a and b. But a and b are relatively prime, so that $d = \pm 1$; moreover d is positive, so it must be 1. Hence $1 = as + bt$.

In what follows the notation "$m \mid n$" means "m divides n" or "m is a factor of n". If m is not a factor of n we write $m \nmid n$. The following theorem is the key to unique factorization.

THEOREM 1.3. *If p is a prime number and $p \mid ab$, then $p \mid a$ or $p \mid b$.*

The possibility that $p \mid a$ *and* $p \mid b$ is not excluded by the theorem.

If $p \mid a$ there is nothing to prove. Suppose then that $p \nmid a$; we shall show that in this case p must divide b. Since p and a are relatively prime there exist integers l and m for which

$$lp + ma = 1, \qquad lpb + mab = b.$$

This follows from the preceding theorem. Since $p \mid ab$ we can write $ab = pq$. The last formula becomes $p(lb + mq) = b$, so that $p \mid b$.

Corollary 1.4. *If a prime number p divides a product $a_1 a_2 \cdots a_n$ of integers, it divides at least one of the a_i.*

For if p divides no a_i, then by Theorem 1.3 it cannot divide any of

$$a_1 a_2, (a_1 a_2)a_3, \cdots, (a_1 a_2 \cdots a_{n-1})a_n.$$

We are now in a position to prove the fundamental theorem stated in the opening paragraph of the chapter. Let m be a positive integer not 1. If it is not prime suppose it factors as $m = m_1 m_2$, where $m_1 > 1$, $m_2 > 1$. If m_1 and m_2 are primes, stop; otherwise repeat the procedure for m_1 and m_2, and continue it for the new factors which appear. Eventually we must arrive at a stage where none of the factors will decompose again. Otherwise m, which is a finite integer, would be the product of an arbitrarily large number of factors all greater than 1.

Thus we arrive at a factorization

$$m = p_1 p_2 \cdots p_r,$$

where each p_i is positive and prime. Suppose

$$m = q_1 q_2 \cdots q_s$$

is any other factorization of m into positive primes. We must prove that the two factorizations differ at most in the order in which the primes appear. Since

$$p_1 p_2 \cdots p_r = q_1 q_2 \cdots q_s$$

it follows from Corollary 1.4 that q_1 must divide one of the p_i. We may suppose it to be p_1, by renumbering the p_i if necessary. Then $q_1 \mid p_1$. Since p_1 and q_1 are positive and prime $p_1 = q_1$. Hence, dividing out $p_1 = q_1$, we obtain

$$p_2 \cdots p_r = q_2 \cdots q_s.$$

This procedure can be repeated with q_2, $\cdots$, until all the prime factors on one side are exhausted. At this stage all the factors on the other side must also be exhausted; otherwise we should have a product of primes on one side equal to 1 on the other. Then $r = s$ and we are done.

If we try to apply the principle of unique factorization to negative integers, we encounter an obvious difficulty in the possible presence of minus signs in the factors. Thus

$$-12 = 2^2(-3) = (-2)\,(-3)\,(-2)$$

are two factorizations of -12 into primes, and these factorizations differ not merely in the order of the factors, but in the factors themselves. For in the first case the factors are $2, 2, -3$; in the second case they are $-2, -3, -2$. This difficulty can be remedied by a slight restatement of the fundamental theorem to include negative numbers. Let 1 and -1 be called *units*. The new statement is this.

THEOREM 1.5. (*The Fundamental Theorem*). *Each integer not zero or a unit can be factored into the product of primes which are uniquely determined to within order and multiplication by units.*

The slight change in the original proof which is needed here will be left to the reader.

2. A general problem.

We are now in a position to state the basic problem of algebraic number theory: if we extend the meaning of "integer" to include a wider class of numbers than the numbers $0, \pm 1, \pm 2, \cdots$ is there still a valid analogue of Theorem 1.5? The nature of the question can best be made plain by examples.

For this purpose we select first the *Gaussian* integers. By such an integer we shall mean a number of the form $a + bi$, where a and b are ordinary integers, and $i = \sqrt{-1}$. To avoid confusion later we shall refer to the ordinary integers as the *rational* integers. Let G denote the set of all Gaussian integers, and J the set of all rational integers. Note that in each set the sum, difference and product of integers are integers.

If α and β are numbers in G we say that α divides β, written $\alpha \mid \beta$, if there is a number γ in G such that $\beta = \alpha\gamma$. An element of G is a *unit* if it divides 1, and hence also every element of G. A number π is *prime* if it is not a unit and if in every factorization $\pi = \alpha\beta$ one of α or β is a unit. With this terminology Theorem 1.5 becomes meaningful for the integers of G.

But is it *true*? It is, as we shall show presently. This fact may strike the reader as only what is to be expected. That such an impression is erroneous we demonstrate by exhibiting another simple class of "integers" for which Theorem 1.5 is meaningful, but false.

Let us now mean by an "integer" any number of the form $a + b\sqrt{-5}$, where a and b are rational integers. Clearly the sum, difference and product of such integers are of the same form. We shall denote the totality of them by H. Define unit and prime just as we did for the Gaussian integers by simply reading H for G wherever the latter occurs. As we shall prove a little later, ± 1 are the only units in H; the numbers $3, 7, 1 + 2\sqrt{-5}, 1 - 2\sqrt{-5}$ will turn out to be prime in H. But observe that

$$21 = 3 \cdot 7 = (1 + 2\sqrt{-5})(1 - 2\sqrt{-5}),$$

so that the factorization of 21 into prime factors is *not* unique to within order and multiplication by units.

It is therefore reasonable to ask for which classes of "integers" the fundamental theorem holds, and for which it does not. In particular how does one explain the discrepancy in behavior between the sets J and G on the one hand and H on the other? The answer to these questions must be postponed until later. For the present we content ourselves with demonstrating the assertions just made concerning the sets G and H.

3. **The Gaussian integers.** If $\alpha = a + bi$ is an element of G its *norm* $N(\alpha)$, or simply $N\alpha$, is defined to be $\alpha\bar{\alpha} = |\alpha|^2 = a^2 + b^2$. ($\bar{\alpha}$ is the complex-conjugate of α). The following list contains the fundamental properties of the norm.

(i) If α is in J as well as in G, then $N\alpha = \alpha^2$.

(ii) $N(\alpha\beta) = N\alpha N\beta$.

(iii) $N\alpha = 1$ if and only if α is a unit.

(iv)

$$N\alpha \begin{cases} = 0 & \text{if } \alpha = 0, \\ = 1 & \text{if } \alpha = \pm 1 \text{ or } \pm i, \\ > 1 & \text{otherwise.} \end{cases}$$

(v) If $N\alpha$ is prime in J, then α is prime in G.

The proof of (i) is obvious since $b = 0$. To prove (ii observe that if $\alpha = a + bi, \beta = c + di$, then

$$(\alpha\beta)\ \overline{(\alpha\beta)} = (\alpha\bar{\alpha})\ (\beta\bar{\beta}).$$

As for (iii), suppose first that α is a unit. Then $\alpha \mid 1$, so $\alpha\beta = 1$ for some β. By (ii) $N\alpha N\beta = N1 = 1$, and $N\alpha \mid 1$. Since $N\alpha$ must be a non-negative integer, $N\alpha = 1$. Conversely if $N\alpha = 1$, $a^2 + b^2 = 1$, so that $a = 0$ or $b = 0$. Then $\alpha = 1, -1, i$ or $-i$, and these are obviously units. This argument also establishes most of (iv); the rest we leave to the reader.

Finally to prove (v), suppose $N\alpha$ is prime and $\alpha = \beta\gamma$. Then $N\alpha = N\beta N\gamma$ is prime in J. So one of $N\beta$ or $N\gamma$ is equal to 1, and by (iii) either β or γ is a unit.

The converse of (v) is false. To see this it is enough to

show that 3 is prime in G, for $N3 = 3^2 = 9$. Suppose $3 = \alpha\beta$. Then $9 = N\alpha N\beta$. If neither α nor β is a unit $N\alpha \neq 1$, $N\beta \neq 1$, so $N\alpha = N\beta = 3$. But this means that if $\alpha = a + bi$, then $a^2 + b^2 = 3$; this is impossible for any pair of integers a, b in J. (why?)

In proving that Theorem 1.5 holds for the Gaussian integers we shall imitate as far as possible the proof already given for rational integers.

THEOREM 1.6. *If α and β are Gaussian integers, $\beta \neq 0$, then there exist two integers π and ρ such that*

$$\alpha = \pi\beta + \rho, \qquad N\rho < N\beta.$$

Consider the number $\dfrac{\alpha}{\beta} = A + Bi$, where A and B are ordinary rational numbers. Choose rational integers s and t such that

$$|A - s| \leq \tfrac{1}{2}, \qquad |B - t| \leq \tfrac{1}{2}.$$

This we can always do by choosing s and t as rational integers nearest to A and B respectively. Now let $\pi = s + ti$, $\rho = \alpha - \pi\beta$.

To show that $N\rho < N\beta$ observe that

$$|\rho| = |\alpha - \pi\beta| = |\alpha - (s + ti)\beta| = |\beta| \left| \frac{\alpha}{\beta} - s - ti \right|$$
$$= |\beta| |(A - s) + (B - t)i| = |\beta| \{(A - s)^2 + (B - t)^2\}^{1/2}$$
$$\leq |\beta| \left\{ \frac{1}{2^2} + \frac{1}{2^2} \right\}^{1/2} < |\beta|.$$

Since $N\rho = |\rho|^2 < |\beta|^2 = N\beta$, the inequality is established.

As an example let $\alpha = 5 - i$, $\beta = 1 + 2i$. Then

$$\frac{\alpha}{\beta} = \frac{(5 - i)(1 - 2i)}{(1 + 2i)(1 - 2i)} = \frac{3}{5} - \frac{11}{5} i,$$

so $A = \frac{3}{5}$, $B = -\frac{11}{5}$. Take $s = 1$, $t = -2$, $\pi = 1 - 2i$,
$\rho = (5 - i) - (1 - 2i)(1 + 2i) = 5 - i - 5 = -i$.
Then

$$5 - i = (1 - 2i)(1 + 2i) - i,$$

and $N(-i) < N(1 + 2i)$.

Let the reader show by an example that, in contrast to Theorem 1.1, π and ρ are *not* uniquely determined.

THEOREM 1.7. *If π is a prime and $\pi \mid \alpha\beta$, then $\pi \mid \alpha$ or $\pi \mid \beta$.*

If $\pi \mid \alpha$ we are done; so suppose $\pi \nmid \alpha$. We shall prove that $\pi \mid \beta$.

By Theorem 1.6 we can find δ and ρ so that

$$\alpha = \delta\pi + \rho, \qquad N\rho < N\pi.$$

Moreover $N\rho \neq 0$, for otherwise $\rho = 0$ so that $\pi \mid \alpha$, contrary to assumption. So $0 < N\rho < N\pi$.

Consider all integers in G which are different from zero and are of the form $\alpha\xi + \pi\eta$. Call the totality of them T. $\rho = \alpha - \pi\delta$ is an integer in T. By property (iv) of norms in G, every element in T has norm at least equal to 1, so there must be one of them $\gamma = \alpha\xi_0 + \pi\eta_0$ which is of least positive norm. Now $\rho = \alpha - \pi\delta$ is in T and has norm less than $N\pi$. Since γ is of least norm, then also $N\gamma < N\pi$. We show next that γ is actually a unit.

Choose θ and ζ so that

$$\pi = \theta\gamma + \zeta, \qquad N\zeta < N\gamma.$$

Since $\zeta = \pi - \theta\gamma = \pi - \theta(\alpha\xi_0 + \pi\eta_0) = \alpha(-\theta\xi_0) + \pi(1 - \theta\eta_0)$, $N\zeta = 0$, for if $N\zeta \neq 0$, then ζ would be an element of T of smaller norm than γ. So $\zeta = 0$ and $\pi = \theta\gamma$, $N\pi = N\theta N\gamma$. One of θ and γ is a unit since π is a prime. But if $N\theta = 1$, then $N\pi = N\gamma$, which contradicts $N\pi > N\gamma$. So θ is not a unit, which means that γ is.

Hence $\gamma = \alpha\xi_0 + \pi\eta_0$ is a unit. Now

$$\alpha\beta\xi_0 + \pi\beta\eta_0 = \gamma\beta.$$

Since $\pi \mid \alpha\beta$ by hypothesis and $\pi \mid \pi\beta\eta_0$, then also $\pi \mid \gamma\beta$. So $\gamma\beta = \pi\tau$ for some τ in G. Then $\beta = \pi(\tau/\gamma)$ and $\pi \mid \beta$, for τ/γ is in G.

To prove that Theorem 1.5 is valid for the integers of G we proceed much as in the case of the rational integers. If α is not a unit or a prime let $\alpha = \alpha_1\alpha_2$, where $N\alpha_1 > 1$, $N\alpha_2 > 1$. Repeat this procedure for α_1 and α_2, and continue it. It must stop sometime, for otherwise $N\alpha$ would be the product of an arbitrarily large number of factors each greater than 1. So $\alpha = \pi_1 \cdots \pi_r$, where the π_i are primes. If also $\alpha = \sigma_1 \cdots \sigma_t$, where the σ_i are primes, then by Theorem 1.7 σ_1 must divide one of the π_i, say π_1. Hence $\sigma_1 = \pi_1\epsilon_1$, where ϵ_1 is a unit. Then

$$\pi_2 \cdots \pi_r = \epsilon_1\sigma_2 \cdots \sigma_t.$$

We can now complete the proof as we did for J.

It remains finally to establish the still unproved statements about H made in the preceding section, namely that ± 1 are the only units, and that $3, 7, 1 + 2\sqrt{-5}, 1 - 2\sqrt{-5}$ are prime numbers in H.

If $\alpha = a + b\sqrt{-5}$, define $N\alpha = \alpha\bar{\alpha} = a^2 + 5b^2$. As before, $N(\alpha\beta) = N\alpha N\beta$. α is a unit if and only if $N\alpha = 1$; the proof goes as in the case of the Gaussian integers. But $a^2 + 5b^2 = 1$ only when $b = 0$, $a = \pm 1$, so $\alpha = \pm 1$ are the only units in H.

To show that 3 is a prime, suppose $3 = \alpha\beta$, where neither α nor β is a unit — that is, $N\alpha \neq 1$, $N\beta \neq 1$. Since $9 = N3 = N\alpha \cdot N\beta$, then $N\alpha = N\beta = 3$, so $a^2 + 5b^2 = 3$. If $b \neq 0$ then $a^2 + 5b^2 > 3$, so b must be zero. But then $a^2 = 3$, which cannot occur for an integer a in J. Similarly if $7 = \alpha\beta$, $N\alpha \neq 1$, $N\beta \neq 1$, then $a^2 + 5b^2 = 7$. If $b^2 \neq 0$,

$b^2 \neq 1$ then $a^2 + 5b^2 > 7$. So either $b = 0$, $a^2 = 7$, which is impossible, or $b = \pm 1$, $a^2 = 2$, which is also impossible.

The numbers $1 \pm 2 \sqrt{-5}$ are prime, for if $1 \pm 2 \sqrt{-5} = \alpha\beta$, then $N(1 \pm 2 \sqrt{-5}) = 21 = N\alpha N\beta$. Unless one of α or β is a unit $N\alpha = 3$ or $N\beta = 3$, and this possibility has already been excluded.

An additional example of a class of "integers" for which unique factorization is valid is given by the set of numbers $a + b\omega$, where $\omega = \frac{1}{2}(-1 + \sqrt{-3})$. The reader who is interested in the details will find them given in Chapter XII of the book of Hardy and Wright listed in the bibliography.

CHAPTER II

THE GAUSSIAN PRIMES

1. Rational and Gaussian primes. It is not difficult to establish the existence of an infinite number of rational primes—that is, primes in J. The simplest proof, due to Euclid, goes as follows. Suppose p_1, p_2, $\cdots$, p_n are known to be prime. Then the number $N = 1 + p_1 p_2 \cdots p_n$ cannot have any one of the p_i as a factor, since then 1 would also have that p_i as a factor. Then any prime factor of N is different from p_1, $\cdots$, p_n. This means that if any finite set of prime numbers is given, there is a prime different from any of them; so there are an infinite number if there is at least one. But 2 is a prime, and the conclusion follows.

Precisely the same proof is valid for Gaussian primes provided only that we can find one prime. But 3 has already been shown to be a Gaussian prime, so that G contains an infinity of primes. We can accomplish considerably more: we shall characterize explicitly all the primes in G in terms of those in J. In order to achieve this we shall need some material from elementary number theory. Actually we shall prove somewhat more than we need for the present purpose. The additional results will find application later.

2. Congruences. In this section we deal only with rational integers.

Let m be an integer not zero. Two integers a and b are said to be *congruent modulo m*, written

$$a \equiv b \pmod{m} \quad or \quad a \equiv b \quad (m),$$

if $m \mid (a - b)$. If a and b are not congruent mod m we write $a \not\equiv b \quad (m)$.

According to Theorem 1.1 every integer a leaves a remainder r, $0 \leq r < |m|$, on division by $|m|$. We shall show that a and b are congruent modulo m if and only if they leave the same remainder on division by $|m|$. First suppose

$$a = q|m| + r, \quad b = q'|m| + r, \quad 0 \leq r < |m|.$$

Then

$$a - b = (q - q')|m|, \quad \pm m \mid (a - b),$$

so that $m \mid (a - b)$. Conversely suppose $a \equiv b \quad (m)$. Let $a = q|m| + r$, $b = q'|m| + r'$, $0 \leq r < |m|$, $0 \leq r' < |m|$. Then

$$a - b = (q - q')|m| + (r - r').$$

Since $|m|$ divides $a - b$, $|m|$ divides $r - r'$. But $-|m| < r - r' < |m|$, so $r - r'$ cannot be divisible by $|m|$ unless $r = r'$.

The following properties of congruences will be used frequently.

(i) If $a \equiv b \quad (m)$, then $b \equiv a \quad (m)$.

(ii) If $a \equiv b \quad (m)$ and $b \equiv c \quad (m)$, then $a \equiv c \quad (m)$.

(iii) If $a \equiv b \quad (m)$, then $ka \equiv kb \quad (m)$ for any integer k.

(iv) If $a_i \equiv b_i \quad (m)$ for $i = 1, 2, \cdots, n$, then

$$a_1 + a_2 + \cdots + a_n \equiv b_1 + b_2 + \cdots + b_n(m),$$

$$a_1 a_2 \cdots a_n \equiv b_1 b_2 \cdots b_n \quad (m).$$

The last part of (iv) is the only one of these properties which is not quite obvious. We verify it when $n = 2$; the general case follows by repeated application of this one. By (iii)

$$a_1 a_2 \equiv b_1 a_2(m), \quad b_1 a_2 \equiv b_1 b_2(m),$$

so that by (ii), $a_1 a_2 \equiv b_1 b_2(m)$.

It is not true that if $ka \equiv kb(m)$, then $a \equiv b(m)$. For example $3 \cdot 2 \equiv 3 \cdot 1(3)$, but $2 \not\equiv 1(3)$. In order to state a correct converse of (iii) we introduce the notion of the *greatest common divisor* (h, k) of two integers h and k; it is simply the largest positive factor common to both h and k. Note that if c is *any* common factor of h and k, then $c \mid (h, k)$; this follows from the fundamental theorem of arithmetic. We can now state

(v). If $ka \equiv kb(m)$, then $a \equiv b(\text{mod } \frac{m}{d})$, where $d = (k, m)$. In particular, $a \equiv b(\text{mod } m)$ if k and m are relatively prime, that is $d = 1$.

Now suppose m to be a positive integer. Since *every* integer leaves on division by m one of the remainders $0, 1, \cdots, m - 1$, every integer is congruent to exactly one of these integers modulo m. Any set of integers such that every integer is congruent to exactly one of them modulo m is called a *complete residue* (or *remainder*) *system modulo m*. It follows that a set of integers is a complete residue system modulo m if and only if it consists of exactly m integers, no two of which are congruent modulo m.

THEOREM 2.1. *If a_1, a_2, $\cdots$, a_m form a complete residue system modulo m, and if $(a, m) = 1$, then aa_1, aa_2, $\cdots$, aa_m also form such a system.*

For if $aa_i \equiv aa_j(m)$, then $a_i \equiv a_j(m)$, by property (v) above.

THEOREM 2.2. *(Fermat). If p is a prime and $(a, p) = 1$, then $a^{p-1} \equiv 1(p)$.*

The number $0, 1, 2, \cdots, p - 1$ form a complete residue system modulo p. Hence $0, a, 2a, \cdots, (p - 1)a$ do also, by the preceding theorem. Now each number on one list is congruent to exactly one on the other. Omitting 0 from each list, since the zeros correspond, we get by (iv)

$$a \cdot 2a \cdots (p-1)a \equiv 1 \cdot 2 \cdots (p-1) \pmod{p},$$

or

$$(p-1)! \, a^{p-1} \equiv (p-1)! \qquad \pmod{p}.$$

By (v) we can divide out $(p-1)!$ from each side to obtain the conclusion.

COROLLARY 2.3. *If p is a prime, then $a^p \equiv a(p)$, for any integer a.*

THEOREM 2.4. (*Wilson*). *If p is a prime, then $(p-1)! \equiv -1(p)$.*

If $p = 2$ or $p = 3$ the conclusion is obvious, so suppose $p > 3$.

Let a be one of the numbers $1, 2, \cdots, p-1$, and let us examine the equation $ax \equiv 1(p)$. Note that $(a, p) = 1$. If x goes through the values $1, 2, \cdots, p-1$ then by Theorem 2.1 ax goes through a complete residue system mod p, excepting 0. Hence there is one and only one x which satisfies the congruence.

Then the numbers $1, 2, \cdots, p-1$ fall into pairs such that the product of any pair is congruent to 1 modulo p. If the members of a pair are equal, say to a, then $a^2 \equiv 1$, $a^2 - 1 \equiv 0, p \mid (a-1)(a+1)$, so $p \mid (a+1)$ or $p \mid (a-1)$. p cannot divide both $a+1$ and $a-1$, since it would divide their difference 2. Hence $a \equiv 1(p)$ or $a \equiv -1(p)$. Since $1 \le a \le p-1$ we have that either $a = 1$ or $a = p-1$.

With the $p-3$ numbers of the set $2, \cdots, p-2$ we can form the product of the $\dfrac{p-3}{2}$ pairs to obtain

$$2 \cdot 3 \cdot 4 \cdots (p-2) \equiv 1 \qquad (p).$$

Then $(p-1)! \equiv p-1 \equiv -1(p)$.

COROLLARY 2.5. *If p is a prime number of the form $4m + 1$, then $p \mid (n^2 + 1)$, where $n = (2m)!$*

Consider the two sets of numbers

$$-1, \quad -2 \quad, \cdots, \quad -2m$$
$$4m, \, 4m - 1, \cdots, 2m + 1.$$

Each element of the lower row is congruent modulo p to the element of the upper row directly above, since their difference is p. Hence

$$4m(4m - 1) \cdots (2m + 1) \equiv (-1)(-2) \cdots (-2m) \quad (p).$$

Since also $(2m)! \equiv (2m)!$, multiplication yields

$$(4m)! \equiv \{(2m)!\}^2 \qquad (p).$$

Let $n = (2m)!$. Since $(4m)! = (p - 1)! \equiv -1$ by Wilson's theorem, it follows that $-1 \equiv n^2 (p)$.

THEOREM 2.6. *If p is a prime and a and b are integers, then*

$$a^p + b^p \equiv (a + b)^p \qquad (mod \ p).$$

By Corollary 2.3, $c^p \equiv c(p)$ for any integer c. Let $c = a + b$. Then $(a + b)^p \equiv a + b$. But also $a^p \equiv a$, $b^p \equiv b$, and from these the result follows.

3. **Determination of the Gaussian primes.** We are now in a position to classify the Gaussian primes. The situation is somewhat complicated by the fact that a rational prime can cease to be a prime in G—for example, $5 = (1 + 2i)(1 - 2i)$; part of our problem is to decide which rational primes are also Gaussian primes.

It is convenient in the classification to call two Gaussian integers *associates*, written $\alpha \sim \beta$, if $\alpha \mid \beta$ and $\beta \mid \alpha$—that is, if $\alpha = \beta\epsilon$ where ϵ is a unit.

THEOREM 2.7. *The Gaussian primes fall into the following three classes*:

1. *all positive rational primes of the form* $4m + 3$ *and their associates in* G;

2. *the number* $1 + i$ *and its associates*;

3. *all integers associated with either* $x + iy$ *or* $x - iy$ *where* $x > 0$, $y > 0$, x *is even, and* $x^2 + y^2$ *is a rational prime of the form* $4m + 1$.

Before proving the theorem we illustrate its application in detecting Gaussian primes. Let $p = 3$. This is in the first of the classes mentioned in the theorem, with $m = 0$; hence 3 is a Gaussian prime. Let $p = 5$. This is of the form $4m + 1$, and $5 = (2 + i)(2 - i)$, so $2 + i, 2 - i$ and their associates are primes, by the third part of the theorem.

To prove the theorem we show first that any prime π in G divides exactly one positive rational prime p. For $N\pi = \pi\bar{\pi}$, so $\pi \mid N\pi$. Let $N\pi = p_1 \cdots p_r$ be the decomposition in J of $N\pi$ into positive primes. Then $\pi \mid p_1 \cdots p_r$. By Theorem 1.7 π divides one of the p_i. So π divides some positive rational prime. It cannot divide two, p and q. For by Theorem 1.2 we can find rational integers l and m such that $lp + mq = 1$. If $\pi \mid p, \pi \mid q$ then $\pi \mid 1$, so π is a unit, not a prime, contrary to hypothesis.

Hence we can get each prime in G once and only once by considering the factorization of all positive rational primes, treated as elements of G.

Now let π be a prime, and p the positive prime for which $\pi \mid p$. Then $N\pi \mid Np$. But $Np = p^2$, since p is a rational integer. Hence $N\pi = p$ or $N\pi = p^2$. If $\pi = x + iy$ then $x^2 + y^2 = p$ or $x^2 + y^2 = p^2$.

Divide p by 4. According to Theorem 1.1 this leaves a remainder of 1, 2 or 3. We consider the three cases separately.

Case 1. $p \equiv 3(4)$. As stated just above, $x^2 + y^2 = p$ or $x^2 + y^2 = p^2$. It will be shown now that the first of these two possibilities cannot occur. Since p is odd, one of x and y, say x, must be even, the other odd; otherwise the sum of their squares would be even. Let $x = 2a$, $y = 2b + 1$. Then if $x^2 + y^2 = p$,

$$p = x^2 + y^2 = 4a^2 + (2b + 1)^2$$
$$= 4(a^2 + b^2 + b) + 1 \equiv 1(4),$$

whereas $p \equiv 3$.

So in this case $x^2 + y^2 = p^2$, and $N\pi = Np$. Since $\pi \mid p$, $p = \pi\gamma$, where γ is in G. Then $Np = N\pi N\gamma$, $N\gamma = 1$, γ is a unit, and $p \sim \pi$.

This accounts for the first part of Theorem 2.7.

Case 2. $p \equiv 2(4)$. In this case $p = 2$, since this is the only even prime. But $2 = (1 + i)(1 - i)$, and $\pi \mid 2$. So $\pi \mid (1 + i)$ or $\pi \mid (1 - i)$. But $N(1 + i) = N(1 - i) = 2$, a rational prime. We showed earlier that if $N\alpha$ is prime so is α. Then $1 + i$ and $1 - i$ are prime. Hence $\pi \sim 1 + i$ or $\pi \sim 1 - i$. Since $\dfrac{1 + i}{1 - i} = i$, $1 + i \sim 1 - i$, and the second part of the theorem is done.

Case 3. $p \equiv 1(4)$. p is of the form $1 + 4m$, so that Corollary 2.5 is applicable and $p \mid n^2 + 1$ for some rational integer n. But $n^2 + 1 = (n + i)(n - i)$ and $\pi \mid p$, so $\pi \mid (n + i)$ or $\pi \mid (n - i)$. But p does not divide $n + i$ or $n - i$, for otherwise one of $\dfrac{n}{p} \pm \dfrac{1}{p}i$ would be a Gaussian integer; this cannot be, for $1/p$ is not a rational integer. Hence π and p are not associated. It follows that $N\pi \neq Np$, so $x^2 + y^2 \neq p^2$. From our earlier remarks, this leaves only the alternative $x^2 + y^2 = p$.

Then $\pi\bar{\pi} = p$. Moreover $\pi = x + iy$ and $\bar{\pi} = x - iy$ are primes, since $N\pi = N\bar{\pi} = p$. They are not associated, for otherwise $x + iy = \epsilon(x - iy)$, where $\epsilon = 1, -1,$ i or $-i$. If $\epsilon = 1, y = 0, x^2 = p$, so p is not a prime. If $\epsilon = -1, x = 0, y^2 = p$, and the same conclusion follows. If $\epsilon = \pm i, x = \pm y$ and p is even. All of these eventualities are impossible, so $x + iy$ and $x - iy$ are not associated.

Finally, since $x^2 + y^2 = p$, one of x and y must be even, the other odd. This completes the account.

4. **Fermat's theorem for Gaussian primes.** It is now reasonable to ask whether the theory discussed in §2 for rational primes has an analogue for Gaussian integers. This is the case, and the theory of congruences and complete residue systems can be carried over. Since we expect to investigate these things later for far more general classes of numbers then the Gaussian integers, we shall only illustrate the kind of thing to be expected by proving the analogue of Fermat's Theorem 2.2.

By $\alpha \equiv \beta \pmod{\gamma}$ or $\alpha \equiv \beta(\gamma)$ we shall now mean that $\gamma \mid (\alpha - \beta)$ in G. Let π be a Gaussian prime.

THEOREM 2.8 (*Analogue of Fermat's theorem*). *If α and π are relatively prime* (*that is, have no common factors except units*), *then*

$$\alpha^{N\pi-1} \equiv 1(\pi).$$

Let p be the unique positive prime p, discussed in the proof of the preceding theorem, for which $\pi \mid p$. There are three cases, corresponding to the three parts of Theorem 2.7.

Case 1. $p \equiv 3(4)$. In this case $N\pi = x^2 + y^2 = p^2$, so we must show $\alpha^{p^2-1} \equiv 1(\pi)$. What we shall prove is that $\alpha^{p^2} \equiv \alpha(p)$. From this the result will follow, for

$$\pi \mid p, \qquad p \mid (\alpha^{p^2} - \alpha), \qquad \pi \mid \alpha(\alpha^{p^2-1} - 1)$$

so $\pi \mid (\alpha^{p^2-1} - 1)$, since $\pi \nmid \alpha$.

Let $\alpha = l + im$. Then $\alpha^p \equiv l^p + i^p m^p(p)$, by the argument used to prove Theorem 2.6. Since p is of the form $4n + 3$, $i^p = -i$. Also $l^p \equiv l$, $m^p \equiv m$ by Corollary 2.3, so

$$\alpha^p \equiv l - im \equiv \bar{\alpha}(p).$$

Similarly

$$\bar{\alpha}^p \equiv \alpha(p),$$

so that

$$\alpha^{p^2} \equiv \bar{\alpha}^p \equiv \alpha(p),$$

as asserted.

Case 2. $p \equiv 2(4)$. In this case $p = 2$, so that $\pi \sim 1 + i$. We may assume $\pi = 1 + i$. Since $N\pi = 2$, what we must prove is that $\alpha^{N\pi-1} = \alpha \equiv 1(\pi)$, or simply that $1 + i$ divides $\alpha - 1$ when $1 + i$ and α are relatively prime. Since $1 + i$ is prime, it suffices to show that if α is a Gaussian integer so is

$$\beta = \frac{\alpha(\alpha - 1)}{1 + i} = \frac{\alpha(\alpha - 1)(1 - i)}{2}.$$

Let $\alpha = a + bi$. Then

$$\beta = \tfrac{1}{2}\{(a^2 - a - b^2 - b + 2ab) \\ + (-a^2 + a + b^2 - b + 2ab)i\}.$$

But

$$a^2 - a - b^2 - b + 2ab \\ = a(a - 1) - b(b + 1) + 2ab$$

$$-a^2 + a + b^2 - b + 2ab \\ = -a(a - 1) + b(b - 1) + 2ab$$

are both even. Hence β is a Gaussian integer.

Case 3. $p \equiv 1(4)$. Now $N\pi = x^2 + y^2 = p$, so we must show that $\alpha^{p-1} \equiv 1(\pi)$. Since $\pi \mid p$ and α, π are relatively prime this will follow if we can prove that $\alpha^p \equiv \alpha(p)$.

Let $\alpha = l + mi$. As in Case 1, $\alpha^p \equiv l^p + i^p m^p(p)$. But p is of the form $4n + 1$, so that $i^p = i$ and $\alpha^p \equiv l + im = \alpha$, as required.

CHAPTER III

POLYNOMIALS OVER A FIELD

1. Divisibility properties of polynomials. By a *number field* F we shall mean a collection of real or complex numbers with the following properties: if α and β belong to F, so do $\alpha + \beta$, $\alpha - \beta$, $\alpha\beta$, and also $\dfrac{\alpha}{\beta}$ if $\beta \neq 0$. Every number field F contains all the rational numbers. For if $\alpha \neq 0$ is in F, so is $\dfrac{\alpha}{\alpha} = 1$; therefore 1, $2 = 1 + 1$, $3 = 1 + 2$, $\cdots$, and all the positive rational integers are in F. But $0 = 1 - 1$ must be contained in F, and hence also $0 - r$, where r is any rational integer. So all rational integers lie in F. Since all quotients of rational integers not zero also belong to F, our statement follows.

The reader can verify that the following sets of numbers form fields: the set R of all rational numbers, the set of all numbers $a + b \sqrt{2}$ with a and b in R, the set of all real numbers, the set of all complex numbers. Observe on the other hand that none of the sets J, G or H considered in the earlier chapters form a field, for they do not contain the set of rational numbers.

In abstract algebra one defines fields of a more general kind; in the present book, however, a "field" will always mean a "number field".

A *polynomial of degree* n, $n \geq 0$, over a field F is an expression of the form

$$p(x) = a_0 + a_1 x + \cdots + a_{n-1} x^{n-1} + a_n x^n$$

where all the coefficients are in F and $a_n \neq 0$. The *product* of two polynomials $p(x)$ and $q(x)$,

$$q(x) = b_0 + b_1 x + \cdots + b_m x^m,$$

is

$$p(x)q(x) = c_0 + c_1x + \cdots + c_k x^k,$$

where

$$c_0 = a_0b_0$$

$$c_1 = a_0b_1 + a_1b_0$$

$$\cdots$$

$$c_i = a_0b_i + a_1b_{i-1} + \cdots + a_{i-1}b_1 + a_ib_0$$

$$\cdots$$

and $k = m + n$.

It is shown in analysis that a polynomial of degree $n \geq 1$ can be factored uniquely into the form

$$p(x) = a_0(x - r_1)(x - r_2) \cdots (x - r_n),$$

where the r_i are numbers which need not belong to the field F containing the coefficients of $p(x)$. For example $p(x) = x^2 + 2x + 3$ is a polynomial over the field R of rational numbers, but in this case $r_1 = -1 + \sqrt{-2}$ $r_2 = -1 - \sqrt{-2}$ and these are certainly not in R.

The numbers $r_1, \cdots, r_n$ are called the *roots* or *zeros* of the polynomial. It follows from the unique factorization just mentioned that a polynomial of degree $n \geq 1$ has at most n distinct roots. It is of course possible for several or all of the roots to be identical. For example

$$x^3 - 3x^2 + 3x - 1 = (x - 1)(x - 1)(x - 1).$$

A polynomial over F is said to be *prime* or *irreducible* over F if it cannot be factored into a product of two or more polynomials

$$p(x) = p_1(x)p_2(x) \cdots p_k(x),$$

where each $p_i(x)$ is of lower degree than $p(x)$ and is itself a polynomial over F. For example $x^2 + 2x + 3$ is irreducible over R, although it is reducible over the field of all complex numbers.

We shall prove that every polynomial over F can be factored into the product of irreducible factors over F, and that the factorization is unique to within order and units. A *unit* is in this case simply a constant—that is, a number from F. Polynomials are relatively prime if they have only units as common factors.

The proof is not unlike that of the fundamental theorem of arithmetic, and we begin by establishing results which parallel the early theorems of Chapter I.

LEMMA 3.1. *Let $f(x)$ and $g(x)$ be polynomials of degrees n and m respectively over a field F, and suppose $n \geq m$. Then for a suitable number c in F the expression*

$$f(x) - cx^{n-m}g(x)$$

is identically zero or is a polynomial of degree less than n.

Let $f(x)$ and $g(x)$ be defined respectively by

$$f(x) = a_n x^n + a_{n-1} x^{n-1} + \cdots + a_0$$
$$g(x) = b_m x^m + b_{m-1} x^{m-1} + \cdots + b_0,$$

where $a_n \neq 0$, $b_m \neq 0$. Define $c = a_n/b_m$. Then

$$f(x) - cx^{n-m}g(x) = (a_n x^n + \cdots) - \frac{a_n}{b_m} x^{n-m}(b_m x^m + \cdots),$$

so that the term in x^n cancels. It is possible for all the terms to cancel, but in any case only terms of lower degree than x^n can survive.

In what follows it is convenient to include 0 as a polynomial, but we give it no degree. The notation $f(x) \equiv 0$ will mean that $f(x)$ is the polynomial zero. A constant *not* zero satisfies our earlier definition of a polynomial of degree n, with $n = 0$.

THEOREM 3.2. *Let $f(x)$ and $g(x) \not\equiv 0$ be polynomials over F. Then there are polynomials $q(x)$ and $r(x)$ over F such that*

$$f(x) = q(x)g(x) + r(x),$$

where $r(x) \equiv 0$ or $r(x)$ is of lower degree than $g(x)$.

If $f(x)$ is identically zero or of lower degree than $g(x)$ we can take $q(x) \equiv 0$, and $r(x)$ to be $f(x)$ itself.

Now regard $g(x)$ as fixed, of degree m. We shall prove the theorem for all $f(x)$ of degree $n \geq m$ by induction. Suppose the conclusion of the theorem to be true for all $f(x)$ of degree between 0 and $n - 1$ inclusive. By the lemma

$$f(x) - cx^{n-m}g(x) = f_1(x)$$

is identically zero or of degree at most $n - 1$. By the first part of the proof if $f_1(x) \equiv 0$, or by the induction hypothesis if $f_1(x) \not\equiv 0$, we have

$$f_1(x) = q_1(x)g(x) + r(x),$$

where $r(x) \equiv 0$ or $r(x)$ is of lower degree than $g(x)$. Then

$$\begin{aligned}
f(x) &= f_1(x) + cx^{n-m}g(x) \\
&= [cx^{n-m} + q_1(x)]g(x) + r(x) \\
&= q(x)g(x) + r(x),
\end{aligned}$$

and the induction is complete.

THEOREM 3.3. *Let $f(x)$ and $g(x)$ be non-zero polynomials over F, relatively prime over F. Then there exist polynomials $s_0(x)$ and $t_0(x)$ over F such that*

$$1 = s_0(x)f(x) + t_0(x)g(x).$$

Consider the set T of all polynomials of the form $s(x)f(x) + t(x)g(x) \not\equiv 0$, where $s(x)$ and $t(x)$ have coefficients in F. Choose in T a member $d(x)$ of lowest degree. $d(x)$ may, of course, be a constant not zero. We shall show that it actually is.

By Theorem 3.2 we can find $q(x)$, $r(x)$ so that

$$r(x) = f(x) - q(x)d(x),$$

where $r(x) \equiv 0$ or $r(x)$ is of degree less than that of $d(x)$. The second of these possibilities is excluded, for $r(x)$ is obviously in T, and no polynomial in T is of lower degree than $d(x)$. So $r(x) \equiv 0$. Hence $f(x) = q(x)d(x)$. Similarly $g(x) = q_1(x)d(x)$ for some polynomial $q_1(x)$. Since $f(x)$ and $g(x)$ are relatively prime, $d(x)$ must be a constant $d \neq 0$. Since d is in T it has a representation

$$d = s_0(x)f(x) + t_0(x)g(x).$$

Divide by d, and the theorem is established.

A polynomial is *monic* if its leading coefficient a_n is 1. By use of Theorem 3.3 it is easy to prove the following two theorems which are analogous respectively to Theorems 1.3 and 1.5. The reader will find it a useful exercise to supply the details of the proofs.

THEOREM 3.4. *If $p(x)$, $f(x)$, $g(x)$ are polynomials over F, $p(x)$ irreducible, and $p(x)$ divides $f(x)g(x)$ over F, then $p(x)$ divides either $f(x)$ or $g(x)$.*

THEOREM 3.5. *Any polynomial $p(x) = a_n x^n + \cdots + a_0$ over F not zero or a constant can be factored into a product*

$$p(x) = a_n p_1(x) \cdots p_r(x)$$

where the $p_i(x)$ are irreducible monic polynomials over F, determined uniquely except for order.

2. The Eisenstein irreducibility criterion.
In this section we shall present a simple and useful test for the irreducibility of a polynomial over the field R of rational numbers.

A polynomial with rational integers as coefficients is *primitive* if the coefficients have no factors other than ± 1 common to all of them. The following theorem is of great importance.

THEOREM 3.6. (*Gauss' Lemma*). *The product of primitive polynomials is primitive.*

Let $a_0 + a_1x + \cdots + a_nx^n$ and $b_0 + b_1x + \cdots + b_mx^m$ be primitive, and let $c_0 + c_1x + \cdots + c_kx^k$ be their product. Assume the product is not primitive. Then all the c_i are divisible by some prime number p. Let a_i and b_j be the *first* coefficients in the two original polynomials (note the order in which the terms were written) which are *not* divisible by p. They must exist, for the polynomials are primitive, and so not all their coefficients can be divisible by p.

Now, by the formula for the product of two polynomials,

$$c_{i+j} = (a_0b_{i+j} + \cdots + a_{i-1}b_{j+1}) + a_ib_j$$
$$+ (a_{i+1}b_{j-1} + \cdots + a_{i+j}b_0).$$

But a_0, a_1, $\cdots$ a_{i-1}, b_0, b_1, $\cdots$ b_{j-1}, and c_{i+j} are all divisible by p. So a_ib_j must also be divisible by p.

Since p is prime, $p \mid a_i$ or $p \mid b_j$. But this contradicts the choice of a_i and b_j as coefficients not divisible by p. Thus the assumption that the c_i have a factor p in common is erroneous, and $c_0 + c_1x + \cdots + c_kx^k$ must be primitive.

As an example, consider the primitive polynomials $x^2 + 3$ and $3x^2 + 7x - 11$. Their product

$$3x^4 + 7x^3 - 2x^2 + 21x - 33$$

is certainly primitive.

THEOREM 3.7. *If a polynomial with rational integral coefficients can be factored over R, it can be factored into polynomials with rational integral coefficients.*

For example,

$$2x^2 + 19x + 35 = (2x + 14)(x + \tfrac{5}{2}),$$

but also

$$2x^2 + 19x + 35 = (x + 7)(2x + 5).$$

The proof goes in two parts. First note that *any polynomial $f(x) \not\equiv 0$ over R can be written uniquely in the form*

$$f(x) = c_f f^*(x),$$

where $f^*(x)$ is primitive and c_f is a positive rational number. For suppose that

$$f(x) = a_n x^n + a_{n-1} x^{n-1} + \cdots + a_0 ,$$

where the a_i are rational numbers. We can write $a_i = \dfrac{b_i}{c}$, where c is the greatest common denominator of all the fractions a_i. Then

$$f(x) = \frac{1}{c} (b_n x^n + b_{n-1} x^{n-1} + \cdots b_0).$$

Now factor out of the expression in parenthesis the largest positive factor common to all the b_i. Then what remains inside the parentheses we call $f^*(x)$, what is outside c_f. Clearly $c_f > 0$, and $f^*(x)$ is primitive by the very manner in which it is defined. As to the uniqueness, if

$$f(x) = c_f f^*(x) = cp(x),$$

where c_f and c are positive and $f^*(x)$, $p(x)$ are primitive, then $f^*(x) \mid p(x)$, $p(x) \mid f^*(x)$, so $f^*(x) = \pm p(x)$, and the $+$ sign must prevail.

We turn to the proof of the theorem. Suppose $f(x) = g(x)h(x)$ over R, where $f(x)$ has integral coefficients. Then

$$c_f f^*(x) = c_g g^*(x) c_h h^*(x),$$

where each of $f(x)$, $g(x)h(x)$ has been written in the form just discussed. So

$$f(x) = c_f f^*(x) = (c_g c_h) g^*(x) h^*(x).$$

But, by Theorem 3.6, $g^*(x)h^*(x)$ is primitive. Moreover the decomposition of $f(x)$ in this form is unique, so $f^*(x) = g^*(x)h^*(x)$ and

$$f(x) = c_f g^*(x) h^*(x).$$

But $f(x)$ and $f^*(x)$ have integral coefficients, and $f^*(x)$ is primitive, so c_f must be a positive integer. This proves the theorem.

THEOREM 3.8. (*Eisenstein's irreducibility criterion*). *Let p be a prime and $f(x) = a_0 + a_1 x + \cdots + a_n x^n$ a polynomial with integral coefficients such that*

$$p \nmid a_n, \quad p^2 \nmid a_0 ; \quad p \mid a_i, \quad i = 0, 1, \cdots n - 1.$$

Then $f(x)$ is irreducible over R.

If $f(x)$ factors over R, then by Theorem 3.7 it has factors with integral coefficients. Suppose that

$$f(x) = (b_m x^m + \cdots + b_0)(c_k x^k + \cdots + c_0),$$

where the b_i, c_j are integers and $m + k = n$, the degree of $f(x)$. Since $a_0 = b_0 c_0$ and $p^2 \nmid a_0$, not both b_0 and c_0 are divisible by p. But $p \mid a_0$, so $p \mid b_0$ or $p \mid c_0$. We may suppose that $p \mid c_0$, $p \nmid b_0$.

Now $a_n = b_m c_k$ is not divisible by p, so c_k is not divisible by it either. Consider the list of coefficients $c_0, c_1, \cdots, c_k$. There must be a smallest value of $r \leq k$ such that c_r is not divisible by p, but $c_0, c_1, \cdots, c_{r-1}$ are so divisible. By the multiplication formula for polynomials

$$a_r = b_0 c_r + b_1 c_{r-1} + \cdots + b_r c_0.$$

All the terms on the right except $b_0 c_r$ are divisible by p.

So a_r is not divisible by it either. But by hypothesis only one of the coefficients a_i is not divisible by p, and that one is a_n. Then $r = n$. Since $r \leq k$, $n \leq k$. But $k + m = n$, so $n \geq k$. The two inequalities can be reconciled only if $n = k$.

Hence one of the proposed factors of $f(x)$ necessarily has the same degree as $f(x)$. Then $f(x)$ must be irreducible.

As an application of Eisenstein's criterion we shall prove the irreducibility over R of two important polynomials. First observe that a polynomial $f(x)$ is irreducible if and only if $f(x + 1)$ is irreducible. For $f(x + 1) = g(x)h(x)$ if and only if $f(x) = g(x - 1)h(x - 1)$.

Let p be a prime and consider the so-called *cyclotomic* polynomial

$$\frac{x^p - 1}{x - 1} = x^{p-1} + x^{p-2} + \cdots + 1.$$

This is irreducible over R if

$$\frac{(x + 1)^p - 1}{(x + 1) - 1} = \frac{(x + 1)^p - 1}{x}$$

is also. But the latter is of the form (why?)

$$x^{p-1} + p(x^{p-2} + \cdots) + p,$$

and the irreducibility follows directly from Theorem 3.8.

As another important example consider the polynomial

$$\frac{x^{p^2} - 1}{x^p - 1} = x^{p(p-1)} + x^{p(p-2)} + \cdots + x^p + 1.$$

Replacing x by $x + 1$ yields

$$x^{p(p-1)} + pq(x),$$

where $q(x)$ has integral coefficients and final term 1. Once again Eisenstein's criterion shows that the polynomial is irreducible over R.

THEOREM 3.9. *If p is a prime number then the polynomials*

$$x^{p-1} + x^{p-2} + \cdots + x + 1$$

and

$$x^{p(p-1)} + x^{p(p-2)} + \cdots + x^p + 1$$

are irreducible over R.

3. **Symmetric polynomials.** Let $x_1, \cdots, x_n$ denote independent variables. By a polynomial in $x_1, \cdots, x_n$ over F we mean a finite sum of the form

$$g(x_1, \cdots, x_n) = \sum_{i_1, i_2, \cdots, i_n} a_{i_1, i_2, \ldots i_n} x_1^{i_1} x_2^{i_1} \cdots x_n^{i_n},$$

where the a's are elements in F and the exponents are non-negative integers. For example, $6x_1 + x_2 x_3 + \frac{1}{5} x_3^2 x_2 + x_1 x_3$ is a polynomial in x_1, x_2, x_3.

A polynomial $g(x_1, \cdots, x_n)$ is *symmetric* if it is unchanged by any of the $n!$ permutations of the variables $x_1, \cdots, x_n$. For example, when $n = 3$ the polynomials $x_1 + x_2 + x_3$ and $x_1 x_2 + x_2 x_3 + x_3 x_1$ are symmetric.

Now let z be still another variable, and define

$$f(z) = (z - x_1)(z - x_2) \cdots (z - x_n)$$
$$= z^n - \sigma_1 z^{n-1} + \sigma_2 z^{n-2} - \cdots (-1)^n \sigma_n.$$

It is easily verified that

$$\sigma_1 = x_1 + x_2 + \cdots + x_n$$
$$\sigma_2 = x_1 x_2 + x_1 x_3 + \cdots + x_2 x_3 + \cdots + x_{n-1} x_n$$
$$\cdots\cdots$$
$$\sigma_i = \text{sum of all products of } i \text{ different } x_j$$
$$\cdots\cdots$$
$$\sigma_n = x_1 x_2 \cdots x_n.$$

The σ_i are called the *elementary* symmetric functions in x_1, $\cdots$, x_n.

We shall assume without proof the following standard theorem concerning symmetric polynomials. The details can be found in most texts on the theory of equations, for example the book of Thomas listed in the bibliography.

THEOREM 3.10. *Every symmetric polynomial in x_1, $\cdots$, x_n over a field F can be written as a polynomial over F in the elementary symmetric functions σ_1, $\cdots$, σ_n. If the coefficients of the first polynomial are rational integers, the same is true of the second.*

For example, let $n = 3$. Then

$$x_1^2 + x_2^2 + x_3^2$$
$$= (x_1 + x_2 + x_3)^2 - 2(x_1 x_2 + x_2 x_3 + x_3 x_1)$$
$$= \sigma_1^2 - 2\sigma_2 .$$

Frequently we shall use the following corollary of Theorem 3.10 rather than the theorem itself.

THEOREM 3.11. *Let $f(x)$ be a polynomial of degree n over F with roots r_1, r_2, $\cdots$, r_n. Let $p(x_1, \cdots, x_n)$ be a symmetric polynomial over F. Then $p(r_1, \cdots, r_n)$ is an element of F.*

As an example, let $f(x) = 2x^2 - 7x + 7$, $F = R$ and $p(x_1, x_2) = x_1^2 + x_2^2$. Then the roots of $f(x)$ are $\dfrac{7 \pm \sqrt{7}i}{4}$ and

$$p(r_1, r_2) = \left(\frac{7 + \sqrt{7}i}{4} \right)^2 + \left(\frac{7 - \sqrt{7}i}{4} \right)^2 = \frac{21}{4} ,$$

which is a rational number, as predicted by the theorem.

To show that Theorem 3.11 follows from Theorem 3.10 is not difficult. By Theorem 3.10 $p(x_1, \cdots, x_n)$ is a polynomial over F in σ_1, σ_2, $\cdots$ σ_n. This means that

$p(r_1, \cdots, r_n)$ is a polynomial in $r_1 + r_2 + \cdots, r_1 r_2 + r_1 r_3 + \cdots, r_1 r_2 \cdots r_n$. But these expressions are simply the coefficients of $f(x)/a_n$ if we write

$$f(x) = a_n(x^n - b_{n-1}x^{n-1} + b_{n-2}x^{n-2} - \cdots \pm b_0).$$

and all the b_i are in F.

An important consequence of Theorem 3.11 is the following corollary.

COROLLARY 3.12. *Let $f(x)$ and $g(x)$ be polynomials over a field F, and let $\alpha_1, \cdots, \alpha_n ; \beta_1, \cdots, \beta_k$ be their respective roots. Then the products*

$$h_1(x) = \prod_{j=1}^{k} \prod_{i=1}^{n} (x - \alpha_i - \beta_j)$$

$$h_2(x) = \prod_{j=1}^{k} \prod_{i=1}^{n} (x - \alpha_i \beta_j)$$

are polynomials in x with coefficients in F.

We can write

$$f(x) = a_n(x - \alpha_1)(x - \alpha_2) \cdots (x - \alpha_n),$$

where a_n is the leading coefficient of $f(x)$. Then

$$f(x - \beta_j)$$
$$= a_n(x - \alpha_1 - \beta_j)(x - \alpha_2 - \beta_j) \cdots (x - \alpha_n - \beta_j)$$
$$= a_n \prod_{i=1}^{n} (x - \alpha_i - \beta_j)$$

Hence

$$a_n^k h_1(x) = \prod_{j=1}^{k} f(x - \beta_j).$$

The product is a polynomial in x whose coefficients are symmetric in $\beta_1, \cdots, \beta_k$. So by Theorem 3.11 its coefficients are in F. If we divide both sides by a_n^k it follows that the coefficients of $h_1(x)$ are in F, since F is a field.

To prove the second part of the theorem note that

$$f\left(\frac{x}{\beta_j}\right) = a_n\left(\frac{x}{\beta_j} - \alpha_1\right) \cdots \left(\frac{x}{\beta_j} - \alpha_n\right),$$

so

$$\beta_j^n f\left(\frac{x}{\beta_j}\right) = a_n(x - \alpha_1\beta_j)\cdots(x - \alpha_n\beta_j),$$

and therefore

$$a_n^k h_2(x) = \prod_{j=1}^{k} \beta_j^n f\left(\frac{x}{\beta_j}\right).$$

The remainder of the proof goes much as before.

CHAPTER IV

ALGEBRAIC NUMBER FIELDS

1. **Numbers algebraic over a field.** Let F be a number field. A number θ is said to be *algebraic* over F if it satisfies a polynomial equation

$$a_n x^n + a_{n-1} x^{n-1} + \cdots + a_0 = 0$$

with coefficients in F. θ need not belong to F. For example $\sqrt{2}$ satisfies $x^2 - 2 = 0$ over R, but $\sqrt{2}$ is not in R.

Suppose now that θ is algebraic over F, and consider all polynomials over F of which θ is a root. Let $p(x)$ be one of lowest degree. Since we can always divide out the leading coefficient, we may assume $p(x)$ to be monic. Then $p(x)$ is called a *minimal polynomial for θ over F*. $p(x)$ is clearly irreducible; otherwise θ would satisfy a polynomial of lower degree.

THEOREM 4.1. *If θ is algebraic over F, it has a unique minimal polynomial.*

Let $p(x)$ be a minimal polynomial, and $q(x)$ any other polynomial over F satisfied by θ. Then

$$q(x) = g(x)p(x) + h(x),$$

where $h(x) \equiv 0$ or $h(x)$ is of lower degree than $p(x)$. Let $x = \theta$. Since $p(\theta) = q(\theta) = 0$ we find $h(\theta) = 0$. Then $h(x) \equiv 0$; otherwise $p(x)$ would not be minimal. So $p(x) \mid q(x)$.

Now if $q(x)$ were any other minimal polynomial of θ over F, the same argument shows that $q(x) \mid p(x)$. Hence $p(x) = \pm q(x)$, and since both are monic, $p(x) = q(x)$, as asserted.

We have proved incidentally the

COROLLARY 4.2. *Any polynomial satisfied by θ over F contains the minimal polynomial of θ as a factor.*

COROLLARY 4.3. *If $f(x)$ and $g(x)$ are relatively prime over F they have no roots in common.*

For if θ were a common root, then by Corollary 4.2 the minimal polynomial of θ over F divides both $f(x)$ and $g(x)$, contrary to the assumption that they have no common factor.

COROLLARY 4.4. *An irreducible polynomial of degree n over F has n distinct roots.*

For suppose the irreducible polynomial $f(x)$ has two roots which are the same. We can write

$$f(x) = a_n(x - r)^2 g(x).$$

Then, taking the derivative of each side,

$$f'(x) = a_n(x - r)^2 g'(x) + 2a_n(x - r)g(x),$$

so that $f(x)$ and $f'(x)$ have a root r in common. By the preceding corollary the polynomials $f(x)$ and $f'(x)$ must have a common factor. Since $f(x)$ is irreducible, it must be that common factor, and $f(x) \mid f'(x)$. But this cannot be, since $f'(x)$ is of lower degree than $f(x)$.

Let θ be algebraic over F, and $p(x)$ its minimal polynomial, say of degree n. Then θ is said to be of *degree n* over F. Let θ_1, θ_2, $\cdots$, θ_n be the roots of $p(x)$, where $\theta_1 = \theta$. By Corollary 4.4 these n numbers are distinct. We call them the *conjugates of θ over F*.

An example. Let $F = R$. By Eisenstein's criterion $x^3 - 2$ is irreducible over R. Let $2^{1/3}$ denote the positive root. Then

$$2^{1/3}, \qquad 2^{1/3}\omega, \qquad 2^{1/3}\omega^2$$

are its conjugates, where $\omega = \frac{1}{2}(-1 + \sqrt{-3})$. For 1 ω, ω^2 are the roots of $x^3 - 1$.

THEOREM 4.5. *The totality of numbers algebraic over a field F forms a field.*

Let α and $\beta \neq 0$ be algebraic over F. We must show that $\alpha + \beta$, $\alpha - \beta$, $\alpha\beta$, $\frac{\alpha}{\beta}$ are themselves algebraic over F— that is, that they satisfy polynomials over F. Let $f(x)$ and $g(x)$ be the minimal polynomials over F for α and β respectively. Form the polynomials $h_1(x)$ and $h_2(x)$ described in Corollary 3.12. They are polynomials over F and are satisfied by $\alpha + \beta = \alpha_1 + \beta_1$ and $\alpha\beta = \alpha_1\beta_1$. Hence the sum $\alpha + \beta$ and the product $\alpha\beta$ are algebraic. Since $-\beta$ satisfies $g(-x)$, $-\beta$ is algebraic. Hence the sum $\alpha + (-\beta) = \alpha - \beta$ is algebraic. Finally, if m is the degree of $g(x)$, then $1/\beta$ satisfies $x^m g(\frac{1}{x})$, so $1/\beta$ is algebraic. By the result for a product, $\alpha \cdot \frac{1}{\beta}$ is also algebraic over F.

Later we shall give an alternative proof of this theorem independent of symmetric functions.

2. **Extensions of a field.** Let F be a field. Then any field K containing F is called an *extension* of F. Every number field, for example, is an extension of the field R of rational numbers.

If θ is algebraic over F, then $K = F(\theta)$ is defined to be the smallest field containing both F and θ. K is called a *simple algebraic extension* of F. Clearly K consists of all quotients $\frac{f(\theta)}{g(\theta)}$, where $f(x)$ and $g(x)$ are any polynomials over F for which $g(\theta) \neq 0$. In our next theorem we shall show that every element of $F(\theta)$ can be written more simply as a polynomial in θ.

THEOREM 4.6. *Every element α of $F(\theta)$ can be written uniquely in the form*

$$\alpha = a_0 + a_1\theta + \cdots + a_{n-1}\theta^{n-1} = r(\theta),$$

where the a_i are in F and n is the degree of θ over F.

Suppose, as we may, that $\alpha = \dfrac{f(\theta)}{g(\theta)}$, where $g(\theta) \neq 0$, and let $p(x)$ be the minimal polynomial for θ over F. Then $p(x)$ is irreducible and $p(x) \nmid g(x)$ (since otherwise $g(\theta) = 0$), so $p(x)$ and $g(x)$ are relatively prime. By Theorem 3.3 there exist polynomials $s(x)$ and $t(x)$ such that $s(x)p(x) + t(x)g(x) = 1$. Let $x = \theta$. Since $p(\theta) = 0$ we find that $\dfrac{1}{g(\theta)} = t(\theta)$, so that

$$\alpha = \frac{f(\theta)}{g(\theta)} = f(\theta)t(\theta)$$

is a polynomial in θ. For simplicity write $\alpha = h(\theta)$.

Now $h(x) = q(x)p(x) + r(x)$, where $r(x) \equiv 0$ or the degree of $r(x)$ is less than that of $p(x)$. Since $p(\theta) = 0$ it follows that

$$\alpha = h(\theta) = r(\theta).$$

Hence α is a polynomial in θ of degree at most $n - 1$.

It remains only to show that $r(x)$ is unique. Suppose also that $\alpha = r_1(\theta)$, where $r_1(x)$ is of degree at most $n - 1$. Then $r(\theta) - r_1(\theta) = 0$ and θ satisfies the polynomial $r(x) - r_1(x)$. But θ satisfies no polynomial of degree less than n. It follows that $r_1(x)$ and $r(x)$ are identical.

Let $\alpha_1, \alpha_2, \cdots, \alpha_n$ be numbers algebraic over F. If $n > 1$, the smallest field $K = F(\alpha_1, \cdots, \alpha_n)$ containing F and the α_i is called a *multiple algebraic extension* of F.

THEOREM 4.7. *A multiple algebraic extension of F is a simple algebraic extension.*

To prove the theorem it is enough to prove that $F(\alpha, \beta)$ is simple when α and β are algebraic over F—that is, that $F(\alpha, \beta) = F(\theta)$ for some θ algebraic over F. For if $K = F(\alpha_1, \alpha_2, \alpha_3)$ we can write it $K = F(\alpha_1, \alpha_2)(\alpha_3)$ and apply the result twice; and similarly for $K = F(\alpha_1, \alpha_2, \cdots, \alpha_n)$.

Let $\alpha_1, \cdots, \alpha_n$; $\beta_1, \cdots, \beta_m$ be the conjugates over F of α and β respectively; we number them so that $\alpha_1 = \alpha$ and $\beta_1 = \beta$. If $k \neq 1$ then $\beta_k \neq \beta$, since conjugates over F are distinct. Hence for each i and each $k \neq 1$ the equation

$$\alpha_i + x\beta_k = \alpha_1 + x\beta_1$$

has at most one solution for x in F. Since there are only a finite number of such equations and hence only a finite number of solutions x, we can choose a number $c \neq 0$ in F different from all solutions x. Then

$$\alpha_i + c\beta_k \neq \alpha + c\beta$$

for all i and all $k \neq 1$. Now let $\theta = \alpha + c\beta$. We shall show that $F(\theta) = F(\alpha, \beta)$ and this will prove the theorem.

First, every element in $F(\theta)$ lies in $F(\alpha, \beta)$, for each element in $F(\theta)$ can, according to Theorem 4.6, be written in the form

$$a_0 + a_1\theta + \cdots + a_{n-1}\theta^{n-1}$$
$$= a_0 + a_1(\alpha + c\beta) + \cdots + a_{n-1}(\alpha + c\beta)^{n-1},$$

and the right hand member is certainly in $F(\alpha, \beta)$.

We must show now that every element of $F(\alpha, \beta)$ lies in $F(\theta)$. This will be achieved if we can prove that α and β are in $F(\theta)$. For if they are, they are of the form $\alpha = r(\theta)$, $\beta = s(\theta)$. Every element of $F(\alpha, \beta)$ is then of the form

$$\frac{u(\alpha, \beta)}{v(\alpha, \beta)} = \frac{u(r(\theta), s(\theta))}{v(r(\theta), s(\theta))}$$

which is certainly in $F(\theta)$. It is enough to show that β is in $F(\theta)$, for then $\alpha = \theta - c\beta$ is also. This we proceed to do now.

Let $f(x)$ and $g(x)$ be the minimal polynomials for α and β respectively. Since $f(\theta - c\beta) = f(\alpha) = 0$, the number β satisfies the equations $g(x) = 0$ and $f(\theta - cx) = 0$. $g(x)$ and $f(\theta - cx)$ have only the root β in common. For the roots of $g(x)$ are $\beta_1, \cdots, \beta_m$ and if $f(\theta - c\beta_i) = 0$ for some $i \neq 1$ then $\theta - c\beta_i$ would be one of the α_i, contrary to the choice of c.

Now $g(x)$ and $f(\theta - cx)$ are polynomials in x *with coefficients in* $F(\theta)$, and they have exactly one root β in common. Let $h(x)$ be the minimal polynomial for β over $F(\theta)$. By Corollary 4.2, $h(x) \mid g(x)$ and $h(x) \mid f(\theta - cx)$ in $F(\theta)$. $h(x)$ cannot be of higher than the first degree, for otherwise $g(x)$ and $f(\theta - cx)$ would have more than one root in common. Hence $h(x) = \gamma x + \delta$, where γ and δ are in $F(\theta)$. But $h(\beta) = 0$, so $\beta = -\delta/\gamma$ is in $F(\theta)$, and we are done.

As an example, suppose it is required to write $R(\sqrt{3}, \sqrt[3]{2})$ as a simple extension $R(\theta)$. The conjugates of $\sqrt{3}$ are $\sqrt{3}, -\sqrt{3}$ and those of $\sqrt[3]{2}$ are $\sqrt[3]{2}, \sqrt[3]{2}\,\omega, \sqrt[3]{2}\,\omega^2$. In this case we can choose c to be 1, and $\theta = \sqrt{3} + \sqrt[3]{2}$. Then $R(\sqrt{3}, \sqrt[3]{2}) = R(\sqrt{3} + \sqrt[3]{2})$.

We shall now give two proofs of the very important fact that every element of a simple, and hence also of a multiple algebraic extension of F is algebraic over F. For one of the proofs we shall use the theory of symmetric functions. For the other we shall use the following lemma from elementary algebra; a proof can be found in Paragraph 27 of Thomas' book listed in the bibliography.

LEMMA 4.8. *If $n < m$ and if the a_{ij} are in a field F, then the system of equations*

$$\sum_{j=1}^{m} a_{ij} x_j = 0, \qquad i = 1, 2, \cdots, n,$$

has a solution for $x_1, \cdots, x_n$ *in* F, *where not all the* x_j *are zero.*

THEOREM 4.9. *If* θ *is algebraic over* F, *so is every element of* $F(\theta)$.

First proof. Let α belong to $F(\theta)$, where θ is of degree n over F. By Theorem 4.6 each of the powers α^i, $i = 0, 1, \cdots, n$, of α can be written

$$\alpha^i = \sum_{j=0}^{n-1} a_{ij}\theta^j,$$

where the a_{ij} are in F. By the preceding lemma we can find in F a set of numbers d_i, not all zero, such that

$$\sum_{i=0}^{n} a_{ij}d_i = 0, \qquad j = 0, 1, \cdots, n - 1,$$

for the number of "unknowns" d_i is greater by one than the number of equations. Then

$$\sum_{i=0}^{n} d_i \alpha^i = \sum_{i=0}^{n} d_i \sum_{j=0}^{n-1} a_{ij}\theta^j$$
$$= \sum_{j=0}^{n-1} \theta^j \sum_{i=0}^{n} a_{ij}d_i = 0,$$

so that α satisfies the polynomial $d_n x^n + d_{n-1}x^{n-1} + \cdots + d_0$ over F.

Second proof. By Theorem 4.6, $\alpha = r(\theta)$. Let

$$f(x) = \prod_{i=1}^{n} (x - r(\theta_i)),$$

where $\theta_1, \theta_2, \cdots, \theta_n$ are the conjugates of θ over F. By Theorem 3.11 the coefficients of $f(x)$ as a polynomial in x are in F. Moreover $f(\alpha) = 0$, so that the proof is complete.

It is now possible to give a new proof of Theorem 4.5 independent of the theory of symmetric functions—as promised earlier. We must show that $\alpha + \beta$, $\alpha - \beta$,

$\alpha\beta$, and $\dfrac{\alpha}{\beta}$, $\beta \neq 0$, are algebraic over F when α and β are. Consider the field $F(\alpha, \beta)$, which contains these four elements in particular. It is a simple algebraic extension, by Theorem 4.7, and every element in it is algebraic over F, by Theorem 4.9.

3. Algebraic and transcendental numbers. A number θ is said to be an *algebraic number* if it is algebraic over the field R of rationals. According to Theorem 4.5 the totality of numbers algebraic over R forms a field. It is reasonable to ask whether this field coincides with the field of all complex numbers,—in other words, whether all numbers are algebraic numbers. We shall answer the question in the negative by exhibiting numbers which are not algebraic; such numbers are called *transcendental*.

LEMMA 4.10. *Let θ be a real algebraic number of degree $n > 1$ over R. Then there is a positive number M such that*

$$\left| \theta - \frac{p}{q} \right| \geq \frac{M}{q^n}$$

for all rational numbers $\dfrac{p}{q}$, $q > 0$.

Let $f(x)$ be the primitive polynomial of lowest degree satisfied by θ; it differs at most by a multiplicative constant from the minimal polynomial for θ, and so is of degree n. Let M' be the maximum of $| f'(x) |$ in the interval $\theta - 1 \leq x \leq \theta + 1$, and let M be the smaller of 1 and $\dfrac{1}{M'}$. For this choice of M the desired inequality is valid. The proof has two parts.

First, suppose that $\left| \theta - \dfrac{p}{q} \right| \geq 1$. Then

$$\left| \theta - \frac{p}{q} \right| \geq M \geq \frac{M}{q^n}$$

for any rational integers p and $q \neq 0$, so we are done.

If $\left| \theta - \dfrac{p}{q} \right| < 1$, the proof is harder. By the law of the mean

$$\left| f(\theta) - f\left(\frac{p}{q} \right) \right| = \left| \theta - \frac{p}{q} \right| \, |f'(\xi)| \leq M' \left| \theta - \frac{p}{q} \right|,$$

where ξ lies between θ and p/q, and hence in the interval $(\theta - 1, \theta + 1)$. Moreover $f(\theta) = 0$, so

$$\left| f\left(\frac{p}{q} \right) \right| \leq M' \left| \theta - \frac{p}{q} \right|.$$

Now $f(\frac{p}{q}) \neq 0$; otherwise $f(x)$ would not be irreducible over R. Since $f(x)$ has integral coefficients and is of degree n, $|f(\frac{p}{q})| = \dfrac{m}{q^n}$, where m is an integer. But $m \geq 1$, so that

$$\frac{1}{q^n} \leq \left| f\left(\frac{p}{q} \right) \right| \leq M' \left| \theta - \frac{p}{q} \right|.$$

Hence

$$\left| \theta - \frac{p}{q} \right| \geq \frac{1}{M'} \frac{1}{q^n} \geq \frac{M}{q^n},$$

by the choice of M.

THEOREM 4.11. (*Liouville*). *There exist transcendental numbers.*

Let $\xi = \displaystyle\sum_{m=1}^{\infty} (-1)^m 2^{-m!}$, and denote by

$$\xi_k = p_k/q_k = p_k/2^{k!}$$

the sum of the first k terms of the series for ξ. Then

$$\left| \xi - \frac{p_k}{q_k} \right| = 2^{-(k+1)!} - 2^{-(k+2)!} + \cdots$$
$$< 2^{-(k+1)!} < 2^{-k \cdot k!} = q_k^{-k}.$$

Suppose that ξ is algebraic of degree $n > 1$ over R. By the preceding inequalities

$$q_k^n \left| \xi - \frac{p_k}{q_k} \right| \leq q_k^{n-k}.$$

Let $k \to \infty$. Then

$$\lim_{k \to \infty} q_k^n \left| \xi - \frac{p_k}{q_k} \right| = 0.$$

From this we can obtain a contradiction. For, by the preceding lemma, there exists a number $M > 0$ such that

$$\left| \xi - \frac{p_k}{q_k} \right| \geq \frac{M}{q_k^n},$$

so $q_k^n \left| \xi - \frac{p_k}{q_k} \right| \geq M > 0$ for all k, contrary to the limit zero just obtained. Then ξ cannot be algebraic of degree $n > 1$.

It follows that ξ is either a rational number—that is, an algebraic number of degree 1—or is transcendental. We shall eliminate the first of these possibilities. Suppose $\xi = \dfrac{p}{q}$, where p and q are rational integers, $q > 0$. Choose an odd k so that $2^{k \cdot k!} > q$. Then the number defined by

$$\eta = 2^{k!} \xi q - 2^{k!} q \sum_{m=1}^{k} (-1)^m 2^{-m!} = 2^{k!} q \sum_{m=k+1}^{\infty} (-1)^m 2^{-m!}$$

is a positive rational integer. But

$$\eta < 2^{k!} q \frac{1}{2^{(k+1)!}} = \frac{q}{2^{k \cdot k!}} < 1,$$

by the choice of k. This contradiction leaves only the alternative that ξ is transcendental.

The number $\xi + \xi i$ is also transcendental. For if it were algebraic and therefore the root of a polynomial with real coefficients, its complex-conjugate $\xi - \xi i$ would also be a root. So the sum $(\xi + \xi i) + (\xi - \xi i) = 2\xi$ would be an algebraic number. This is impossible, since ξ is not an algebraic number.

For the reader familiar with the notion of denumerability a simpler proof of Theorem 4.11 is available. However, it does not yield any explicit examples of transcendental numbers. Briefly, it runs as follows. The totality of polynomials with rational coefficients is denumerable. Each has a finite number of roots, so the totality of algebraic numbers is denumerable. But the totality of complex numbers is non-denumerable, so that some of them must fail to be algebraic.

The problem of testing particular numbers for thanscendence is a very difficult one. It was already known in the last century that e and π are transcendental (simple proofs can be found in Landau, Vorlesungen III; see the bibliography). But it is only recently that such numbers as e^π and $2^{\sqrt{2}}$ have been shown to be transcendental. This is a consequence of a far reaching theorem of Gelfond and Schneider which we state here without proof. An account of it is given by E. Hille in the American Mathematical Monthly vol. 49(1942), pp. 654–661.

THEOREM 4.12. *Let α and β be algebraic numbers different from 0 and 1. If the number*

$$\eta = \frac{\log \alpha}{\log \beta}$$

is not rational, then it is also transcendental.

We shall illustrate the theorem by proving from it that $2^{\sqrt{2}}$ is transcendental. Suppose, on the contrary, that $\alpha = 2^{\sqrt{2}}$ is algebraic. Let $\beta = 2$. Since

$$\eta = \frac{\log 2^{\sqrt{2}}}{\log 2} = \sqrt{2}$$

is irrational, then η must be transcendental. This is obviously false, so that α cannot be algebraic.

A similar argument proves that e^{π} is transcendental, provided we first observe that e^{π} can also be written i^{-2i}. Let the reader complete the proof.

CHAPTER V

BASES

1. **Bases and finite extensions.** Let F be a number field and K an extension of it. A set of numbers $\alpha_1, \alpha_2, \cdots, \alpha_r$ in K is said to be *linearly dependent* (*over F*) if it is possible to find a set of numbers $c_1, c_2, \cdots, c_r$ in F, not all zero, such that

$$. \; c_1\alpha_1 + c_2\alpha_2 + \cdots + c_r\alpha_r = 0.$$

Otherwise the numbers $\alpha_1, \alpha_2, \cdots, \alpha_r$ are called *linearly independent*.

A set of numbers $\beta_1, \beta_2, \cdots, \beta_s$ in K is said to form a *basis** for K over F if for each element β in K there exists a unique set of numbers $d_1, d_2, \cdots, d_s$ in F such that

$$\beta = d_1\beta_1 + d_2\beta_2 + \cdots d_s\beta_s.$$

Observe that the β_i are linearly independent, for otherwise 0 has a representation

$$0 = e_1\beta_1 + e_2\beta_2 + \cdots + e_s\beta_s,$$

where not all the e_i are zero, and also the representation

$$0 = 0\cdot\beta_1 + 0\cdot\beta_2 + \cdots + 0\cdot\beta_s,$$

contrary to the requirement of uniqueness.

LEMMA 5.1. *If K has a basis of s elements over F, then any t numbers in K, $t > s$, are linearly dependent over F.*

Let $\beta_1, \cdots, \beta_s$ be a basis for K and let $\alpha_1, \cdots, \alpha_t$ be t numbers in K. By the definition of a basis we can find numbers a_{ij} in F such that

$$\alpha_i = \sum_{j=1}^{s} a_{ij}\beta_j, \qquad i = 1, \cdots, t.$$

* This is also called a *fundamental system* in the older literature.

47

Since $t > s$ we can invoke Lemma 4.8 to conclude that there exist numbers c_i in F, not all zero, such that

$$\sum_{i=1}^{t} a_{ij} c_i = 0, \qquad j = 1, \cdots, s.$$

It follows that

$$\sum_{i=1}^{t} c_i \alpha_i = \sum_{i=1}^{t} c_i \sum_{j=1}^{s} a_{ij} \beta_j$$

$$= \sum_{j=1}^{s} \beta_j \sum_{i=1}^{t} a_{ij} c_i = 0,$$

so that the α_i are linearly dependent.

THEOREM 5.2. *If* $\alpha_1, \alpha_2, \cdots, \alpha_t$ *and* $\beta_1, \beta_2, \cdots, \beta_s$ *are both bases for K over F, then $s = t$.*

If $s \neq t$ we can suppose $t > s$. By the preceding lemma the α_i must be linearly dependent. This is impossible, since they form a basis.

We have shown that if K has a basis over F, every basis has the same number n of elements. n is called the *degree* of K over F, and K is called a *finite extension* of degree n over F. We write $n = (K/F)$.

LEMMA 5.3. *If K is a finite extension of degree n over F, then any n linearly independent elements in K form a basis.*

Let $\beta_1, \cdots, \beta_n$ be a basis for K over F, and let $\alpha_1, \cdots, \alpha_n$ be a set of n linearly independent elements of K. We wish to show that every element α can be represented in the form

$$\alpha = d_1 \alpha_1 + d_2 \alpha_2 + \cdots d_n \alpha_n.$$

That such a representation is unique follows directly from the linear independence of the α_i.

Since the β_i form a basis we can write

$$\alpha_i = \sum_{j=1}^{n} a_{ij} \beta_j, \qquad i = 1, \cdots, n;$$

$$\alpha = \sum_{j=1}^{n} a_{oj} \beta_j.$$

By Lemma 4.8 we can find c_i, not all zero, in F such that

$$\sum_{i=0}^{n} a_{ij} c_i = 0, \qquad j = 1, \cdots, n.$$

Then

$$c_0 \alpha + c_1 \alpha_1 + c_2 \alpha_2 + \cdots + c_n \alpha_n$$
$$= \sum_{i=0}^{n} c_i \sum_{j=1}^{n} a_{ij} \beta_j = \sum_{j=1}^{n} \beta_j \sum_{i=0}^{n} c_i a_{ij} = 0.$$

Now $c_0 \neq 0$, since otherwise $c_1 \alpha_1 + \cdots + c_n \alpha_n = 0$ and, on account of the linear independence of the α_i, all the c_i would be zero. Hence

$$\alpha = -\frac{c_1}{c_0} \alpha_1 - \frac{c_2}{c_0} \alpha_2 - \cdots - \frac{c_n}{c_0} \alpha_n,$$

as required.

THEOREM 5.4. *If $\alpha_1, \cdots, \alpha_n$ is a basis for K over F and*

$$\beta_j = \sum_{i=1}^{n} a_{ij} \alpha_i, \qquad j = 1, 2, \cdots n,$$

where the a_{ij} are in F, then $\beta_1, \cdots, \beta_n$ is also a basis if and only if the determinant $|a_{ij}|$ is not zero.

First suppose $|a_{ij}| \neq 0$. By the preceding results it is enough to show that the β_j are linearly independent. Suppose $\sum_{j=1}^{n} c_j \beta_j = 0$, where the c_j are in F. Then

$$0 = \sum_{j=1}^{n} c_j \sum_{i=1}^{n} a_{ij} \alpha_i = \sum_{i=1}^{n} \alpha_i \sum_{j=1}^{n} c_i a_{ij}.$$

Since the α_i are linearly independent

$$\sum_{j=1}^{n} c_j a_{ij} = 0, \qquad i = 1, \cdots, n.$$

The determinant $|a_{ij}| \neq 0$, so that all the c_j must vanish.

Conversely, suppose $|a_{ij}| = 0$. Then the equations immediately preceding are known to have a solution with the c_j in F, and not all zero. Retracing our steps, we find

$$\sum_{j=1}^{n} c_j \beta_j = 0,$$

so that the β_j are not linearly independent.

2. Properties of finite extensions.

Next we propose to show that finite extensions and simple algebraic extensions of a field are the same thing.

LEMMA 5.5. *If K is a finite extension of F then every element α of K is algebraic over F.*

Let $n = (K/F)$. By Lemma 5.1 the $n + 1$ numbers $1, \alpha, \alpha^2, \cdots, \alpha^n$ are linearly dependent, so that $c_0, c_1, \cdots, c_n$ not all zero exist in F such that

$$c_0 + c_1\alpha + \cdots + c_n\alpha^n = 0.$$

It follows that α satisfies a polynomial over F.

THEOREM 5.6. *An extension K of F is finite if and only if it is a simple algebraic extension.*

First suppose that K is a finite extension of F, and let $\alpha_1, \cdots, \alpha_n$ be a basis. Then $K = F(\alpha_1, \cdots, \alpha_n)$. By the preceding lemma each α_i is algebraic over F. It follows from Theorem 4.7 that K is a simple algebraic extension of F.

Suppose conversely that $K = F(\theta)$, where θ is of degree n over F. By Theorem 4.6 the numbers $1, \theta, \cdots, \theta^{n-1}$

form a basis for K over F. This completes the proof. Note that (K/F) is the same as the degree of θ over F.

THEOREM 5.7. *If K is finite over F, and E over K, then E is finite over K. Moreover*

$$(E/F) = (E/K)\cdot(K/F).$$

Let $\alpha_1, \cdots, \alpha_n$ be a basis for K over F, and $\beta_1, \cdots, \beta_m$ for E over K. It is easily verified that the mn products $\alpha_i\beta_j$ are linearly independent. We shall show that they form a basis for E over F.

If α is any number in E it can be written $\alpha = \sum_{i=1}^{m} \gamma_i\beta_i$, where the γ_i are in K, for the β_i form a basis of E over K. Similarly each γ_i can be written $\sum_{j=1}^{n} a_{ij}\alpha_j$, where the a_{ij} are in F, for the α_j are a basis of K over F. Then

$$\alpha = \sum_{i=1}^{m} \beta_i \sum_{j=1}^{n} a_{ij}\alpha_j = \sum_{i=1}^{m} \sum_{j=1}^{n} a_{ij}\alpha_j\beta_i,$$

as required. The formula given in the theorem follows immediately.

We can now prove the following refinement of Lemma 5.5.

COROLLARY 5.8. *If K is of degree n over F, then any element α of K is algebraic over F, of degree dividing n.*

Let $E = F(\alpha)$. Then

$$n = (K/F) = (K/E)(E/F).$$

Hence (E/F) divides n. But, by the remark at the end of the proof of Theorem 5.6, the degree of E over F is the same as the degree of α over F.

THEOREM 5.9. *If α satisfies the equation*

$$\alpha_n x^n + \alpha_{n-1} x^{n-1} + \cdots + \alpha_o = 0$$

where the α_i are algebraic over F, then α is algebraic over F.

Let $E = F(\alpha_1, \cdots, \alpha_n)$. This can be written as a simple algebraic extension of F. By Theorem 5.6, E is a finite extension of F. Moreover $E(\alpha)$ is a finite extension of E and hence, by Theorem 5.7, a finite extension of F. Then α lies in a finite extension of F. By the preceding corollary α is algebraic over F.

In much of what follows in this book the field F will be taken to be the field R of rational numbers. An *algebraic number field* is any *finite* (hence simple) *extension of R*. The totality of algebraic numbers, while it forms a field (Theorem 4.5), does not form an algebraic number field. For suppose this field were of degree n over R. The presence in it of an element of degree greater than n would contradict Corollary 5.8. But it is easy to produce an algebraic number of degree $n + 1$. The polynomial $x^{n+1} - 2$ is irreducible over R, by Eisenstein's criterion, so $2^{1/n+1}$ is of degree $n + 1$.

3. Conjugates and discriminants. The reader is reminded that the conjugates over F of a number α algebraic over F are the roots of the minimal polynomial of α over F. We find it useful to define a new concept of conjugacy, and to discuss its relation to the old.

Let $K = F(\theta)$ be a finite extension of degree n over F, and suppose α to be a number in K. By Corollary 5.8 the degree m of α over F divides n. According to Theorem 4.6 α can be written uniquely in the form

$$\alpha = \sum_{i=0}^{n-1} c_i \theta^i = r(\theta).$$

Let $\theta_1, \cdots, \theta_n$ be the conjugates of θ over F. Then the numbers

$$\alpha_i = r(\theta_i), \qquad i = 1, \cdots, n,$$

are called the *conjugates of* α *for* $F(\theta)$. So α has n conjugates in the new sense, but m in the old, where $m \mid n$.

It is easily verified that the conjugates of $\alpha\beta$ and $\alpha + \beta$ for $F(\theta)$ are respectively $\alpha_1\beta_1 , \cdots \alpha_n\beta_n$, and $\alpha_1 + \beta_1 , \cdots ,$ $\alpha_n + \beta_n$.

The relation between the old and the new conjugates is settled by our next theorem.

THEOREM 5.10. (i) *The conjugates of* α *for* $F(\theta)$ *are the conjugates over* F *each repeated* n/m *times.* (ii) α *is in* F *if and only if all conjugates for* $F(\theta)$ *are the same.* (iii) $F(\alpha) = F(\theta)$ *if and only if all its conjugates for* $F(\theta)$ *are distinct.*

As we showed in the second proof of Theorem 4.9, the polynomial

$$f(x) = \prod_{1}^{n} (x - r(\theta_i))$$

is a polynomial over F, and $f(\alpha) = 0$. ($f(x)$ is called the *field polynomial* for α). Let $g(x)$ be the minimal polynomial for α over F. By Corollary 4.2, $g(x) \mid f(x)$, so we can write

$$f(x) = [g(x)]^s h(x),$$

where $g(x)$ and $h(x)$ are relatively prime. We prove that $h(x) \equiv 1$. Note that if $h(x)$ is a constant at all it must be 1, since $g(x)$ and $f(x)$ are monic.

If $h(x)$ is not a constant it has one of the $r(\theta_i)$ as a root. Then $h(r(x))$ vanishes when x equals one of the θ_i . Let $p(x)$ be the minimal polynomial for θ, and hence for θ_i . Then $p(x) \mid h(r(x))$. It follows that $h(r(x))$ vanishes for all the θ_i , in particular for θ. So $h(r(\theta)) = h(\alpha) = 0$. This is impossible by Corollary 4.3, since $g(\alpha) = 0$ and $g(x), h(x)$ are relatively prime.

Hence $f(x) = [g(x)]^s$. Since m is the degree of α over F, $s = n/m$, the field polynomial is a power of the minimal polynomial. This proves (i).

As for (ii), if α is in F then $g(x) = x - \alpha$, $m = 1$, $s = n/m = n$, and $f(x) = (x - \alpha)^n$, so all the conjugates are the same. Conversely, if all the conjugates are the same $f(x) = (x - \alpha)^n$, so $s = n$, $m = 1$, and α is in F.

Finally, we prove (iii). Note that

$$\left(\frac{F(\theta)}{F}\right) = \left(\frac{F(\theta)}{F(\alpha)}\right) \cdot \left(\frac{F(\alpha)}{F}\right),$$

so $F(\theta) = F(\alpha)$ if and only if $m = n$, $s = 1$. In this case $f(x) = g(x)$ and all the conjugates are distinct. On the other hand, if the conjugates are distinct $s = 1$, $m = n$, and the result follows. The theorem is proved.

Now suppose $K = F(\theta)$ is of degree n over F, and let $\alpha_1, \cdots, \alpha_n$ be a basis. Denote by $\alpha_j^{(i)}$, $i = 1, \cdots, n$, the conjugates of α_j for K. The *discriminant* of the set $\alpha_1, \cdots, \alpha_n$ is defined by

$$\Delta[\alpha_1, \cdots \alpha_n] = |\alpha_j^{(i)}|^2,$$

where $|\alpha_j^{(i)}|$ is the determinant

$$\begin{vmatrix} \alpha_1^{(1)} & \alpha_2^{(1)} & \cdots & \alpha_n^{(1)} \\ \cdots\cdots\cdots\cdots\cdots\cdots\cdots \\ \alpha_1^{(n)} & \alpha_2^{(n)} & \cdots & \alpha_n^{(n)} \end{vmatrix}.$$

If

$$\beta_k = \sum_{j=1}^{n} c_{jk}\alpha_j, \qquad k = 1, \cdots, n,$$

is another basis, then $|c_{jk}| \neq 0$, by Theorem 5.4. By the multiplication of determinants we arrive at the important formula

$$(5.1) \qquad \Delta[\beta_1, \cdots, \beta_n] = |c_{jk}|^2 \Delta[\alpha_1, \cdots, \alpha_n].$$

By Theorem 4.6 a particular basis for $F(\theta)$ is 1, θ, θ^2, $\cdots$, θ^{n-1}. If we use the fact that $(\theta^i)^{(j)}$ (the j-th conjugate of θ^i) is the same as $(\theta^{(j)})^i$ (the i-th power of $\theta^{(j)}$) we find that

$$D(\theta) = \Delta[1, \theta, \cdots, \theta^{n-1}]$$

$$= \begin{vmatrix} 1 & \theta^{(1)} & (\theta^{(1)})^2 & \cdots & (\theta^{(1)})^{n-1} \\ \cdots\cdots\cdots\cdots\cdots\cdots\cdots\cdots \\ 1 & \theta^{(n)} & (\theta^{(n)})^2 & \cdots & (\theta^{(n)})^{n-1} \end{vmatrix}^2,$$

and this Vandermonde determinant is known to have the value*

$$(5.2) \qquad D(\theta) = \prod_{1 \le i < j \le n} (\theta^{(i)} - \theta^{(j)})^2.$$

$D(\theta) \neq 0$ since the conjugates of θ for $F(\theta)$ are necessarily distinct. Since $D(\theta)$ is symmetric in the $\theta^{(i)}$ it is an element of F. It is obviously positive if all the $\theta^{(i)}$ are real. In (5.1) take $\alpha_i = \theta^{i-1}$, $i = 1, \cdots, n$. Then

$$\Delta[\beta_1, \cdots, \beta_n] = |c_{jk}|^2 D(\theta)$$

is an element of F. We have proved

THEOREM 5.11. *The discriminant of any basis for $F(\theta)$ is in F and is never zero. If F, θ and the conjugates of θ are all real then the discriminant of any basis is positive.*

4. **The cyclotomic field.** We shall now discuss a special kind of field which is of great importance. This will serve as an illustration of the theory which precedes, and will also be useful in our later work.

Let p be an odd prime. By Theorem 3.9 the cyclotomic polynomial $x^{p-1} + x^{p-2} + \cdots + 1$ is irreducible over R. Hence any root ζ generates a field $R(\zeta)$ of degree $p - 1$ over R. $R(\zeta)$ is called a *cyclotomic* field.

* Uspensky, Theory of Equations, p. 214.

If ζ is any root then ζ, ζ^2, $\cdots$, ζ^{p-1} are all the roots because

(i) none of the ζ^s is 1, for otherwise ζ would satisfy a polynomial $x^s - 1$ of degree lower than $p - 1$;

(ii) they are all different, for the same reason; and

(iii) they all satisfy $x^p - 1 = 0$, since $(\zeta^s)^p - 1 = (\zeta^p)^s - 1 = 0$. This set of roots ζ, $\cdots$, ζ^{p-1} are called the *primitive p^{th} roots* of unity. Since they lie on a circle of unit radius and none of them is ± 1, they are all imaginary. The conjugates of ζ for $R(\zeta)$ are then simply ζ, ζ^2, $\cdots$, ζ^{p-1}. Hence we can write $\zeta^{(i)} = \zeta^i$. We shall use this information to compute $D(\zeta)$.

By Theorem 4.6 with $n = p - 1$, a basis for $R(\zeta)$ is 1, ζ, $\cdots$, ζ^{p-2}. By (5.2)

$$D(\zeta) = \prod_{0 \le i < j \le p-2} (\zeta^i - \zeta^j)^2.$$

Another basis is ζ, ζ^2, $\cdots$, ζ^{p-1} for this set of numbers is linearly independent over R. The relation between the two bases is given by

$$
\begin{aligned}
\zeta &= 0 + \zeta \\
\zeta^2 &= 0 + 0 + \zeta^2 \\
&\quad . \quad . \quad . \\
\zeta^{p-2} &= 0 + 0 + \cdots + \zeta^{p-2} \\
\zeta^{p-1} &= 1 - \zeta - \zeta^2 - \cdots - \zeta^{p-2},
\end{aligned}
$$

so the determinant $|c_{jk}|$ has the square 1. Hence, by (5.1) and (5.2),

$$(5.3) \quad D(\zeta) = \Delta[\zeta, \zeta^2, \cdots, \zeta^{p-1}] = \prod_{1 \le i < j \le p-1} (\zeta^i - \zeta^j)^2.$$

THEOREM 5.12. *If ζ is a primitive p^{th} root of unity, p an odd prime, then*

$$D(\zeta) = (-1)^{(p-1)/2} p^{p-2}.$$

Since $\zeta, \cdots, \zeta^{p-1}$ are all the primitive roots we have

$$(5.4) \quad \frac{x^p - 1}{x - 1} = x^{p-1} + \cdots + 1 = \prod_{i=1}^{p-1} (x - \zeta^i).$$

Differentiate the right- and left-hand members, and let $x = \zeta^j$. Since $\zeta^p = 1$, we find that

$$(5.5) \quad -\frac{p\zeta^{p-j}}{1 - \zeta^j} = \prod_{\substack{i=1 \\ i \neq j}}^{p-1} (\zeta^j - \zeta^i).$$

By (5.4) with $x = 0$ and $x = 1$ respectively it follows that

$$\prod_{j=1}^{p-1} \zeta^{p-j} = \zeta \cdot \zeta^2 \cdots \zeta^{p-1} = (-1)^{p-1}$$

and

$$\prod_{j=1}^{p-1} (1 - \zeta^j) = p.$$

Hence by (5.5),

$$p^{p-2} = \prod_{j=1}^{p-1} \prod_{\substack{i=1 \\ i \neq j}}^{p-1} (\zeta^j - \zeta^i).$$

In the final product $i < j$ for half the factors and $j < i$ for the other half. There are $(p - 1)(p - 2)$ factors in all. Hence the last product is

$$p^{p-2} = (-1)^{(p-1)(p-2)/2} \prod_{1 \leq i < j \leq p-1} (\zeta^i - \zeta^j)^2.$$

But p is odd, so

$$(-1)^{(p-1)(p-2)/2} = (-1)^{(p-1)/2}.$$

If we combine these facts with the formula (5.3), the theorem follows.

CHAPTER VI

ALGEBRAIC INTEGERS AND INTEGRAL BASES

1. Algebraic integers. Let $R(\theta)$ be an algebraic number field. What shall we mean by an *integer* in this field? With the example of the Gaussian integers as the "integers" in $R(i)$ before us, the following conditions seem reasonable to demand of our definition:

(i) if α and β are integers in $R(\theta)$, so are $\alpha + \beta$, $\alpha - \beta$, $\alpha\beta$;

(ii) if α is an integer in $R(\theta)$ and is also a rational number, then it is a rational integer;

(iii) if α is an integer so are its conjugates; (in which of the two senses "conjugate" is to be taken is clearly a matter of indifference here.)

It turns out that the following definition meets all the requirements: an algebraic number is an *algebraic integer* if its minimal polynomial has only rational integers as coefficients. Since a minimal polynomial is monic α must satisfy an equation

$$p(x) = x^n + a_{n-1}x^{n-1} + a_{n-2}x^{n-2} + \cdots + a_0 = 0,$$

where the a_i are rational integers. It follows that the requirement (iii) is automatically fulfilled. To see that (ii) is also fulfilled is simple, for if α satisfies $p(x)$ and is rational, then its degree over R is 1, so $n = 1$, and so its minimal polynomial is simply $x + a_0 = 0$.

To prove that (i) holds is somewhat more complicated.

LEMMA 6.1. *If α satisfies any monic polynomial $f(x)$ with rational integral coefficients then α is an algebraic integer.*

Let $p(x)$ be the minimal polynomial for α over R. It is monic. We shall prove that *all* its coefficients are integers. It will follow that α is an algebraic integer.

By Corollary 4.2. $f(x) = p(x)q(x)$, where $q(x)$ is a polynomial over R. The proof of Theorem 3.7 shows that $f(x) = c_f p^*(x)q^*(x)$, where $p(x) = c_p p^*(x)$, and $p^*(x)$ and $q^*(x)$ are primitive. Since $f(x)$ is monic it is primitive, and $c_f = 1$. $p^*(x)$ and $q^*(x)$ have integral coefficients, and must therefore be monic, for their product $f(x)$ is monic. But $p(x)$ is also monic. Hence $c_p = 1$, and $p(x) = p^*(x)$ has integral coefficients.

THEOREM 6.2. *If $R(\theta)$ is an algebraic number field, then the integers in it have the properties* (i), (ii), (iii) *specified above.*

Properties (ii) and (iii) have already been verified; only (i) remains. Let $\alpha_1, \cdots, \alpha_n; \beta_1, \cdots, \beta_k$ be the conjugates over R of the algebraic integers $\alpha = \alpha_1$ and $\beta = \beta_1$ respectively.

The elementary symmetric functions in $\beta_1, \cdots, \beta_k$ are rational integers since, except for sign, they are the ceofficients of the minimal polynomial for the algebraic integer β. It follows from the second part of Theorem 3.10 that *any symmetric polynomial in $\beta_1, \cdots, \beta_k$ with rational integral coefficients is a rational integer.*

Now let $f(x)$ be the minimal polynomial for the integer α; and define

$$h(x) = \prod_{j=1}^{k} f(x - \beta_j).$$

This is a polynomial in x. Since $f(x)$ has integral coefficients, the coefficients of $h(x)$ are symmetric polynomials in the β_j with rational integral coefficients. By the italicized remark above, $h(x)$ has rational integers for coefficients. Since $f(x)$ is monic, so is $h(x)$. Finally

$$h(\alpha + \beta) = h(\alpha_1 + \beta_1)$$
$$= f(\alpha_1 + \beta_1 - \beta_1) \prod_{j=2}^{k} f(\alpha_1 + \beta_1 - \beta_j) = 0,$$

since $f(\alpha_1) = 0$. So by Lemma 6.1 $\alpha + \beta$ is an algebraic integer. It belongs to $R(\theta)$, since α and β do. The proofs for $\alpha - \beta$, $\alpha\beta$ are similar, and will be omitted (cf. the first proof of Theorem 4.5).

Note incidentally that this proof shows that $\alpha + \beta$, $\alpha - \beta$, $\alpha\beta$ are algebraic integers when α and β are, even if we do not suppose that α and β lie in the given field $R(\theta)$. Now define a *ring* to be a set of numbers which contains $\alpha + \beta$, $\alpha - \beta$, $\alpha\beta$ when it contains α and β. Then we have

COROLLARY 6.3. *The totality of algebraic integers forms a ring. So does the totality of algebraic integers contained in any algebraic number field.*

THEOREM 6.4. *If α satisfies an equation*

$$f(x) = x^n + \gamma_{n-1}x^{n-1} + \gamma_{n-2}x^{n-2} + \cdots + \gamma_0 = 0$$

where the γ_i are algebraic integers, then α is an algebraic integer.

Let $\gamma_j^{(i)}$ denote the conjugates of γ_j over R. Form the product

$$h(x) = \Pi(x^n + \gamma_{n-1}^{(i_1)}x^{n-1} + \gamma_{n-2}^{(i_2)}x^{n-2} + \cdots + \gamma_0^{(i_n)}),$$

over all these conjugates. By the now familiar argument on symmetric functions the coefficients of $h(x)$ are in R. But they are also algebraic integers since they consist of sums of products of the $\gamma_j^{(i)}$. By property (ii) they are rational integers. Since $f(x) \mid h(x)$, $h(\alpha) = 0$. Finally $h(x)$ is monic, so Lemma 6.1 can be invoked to complete the proof.

We conclude this section with a simple but very useful property of integers.

THEOREM 6.5. *If θ is an algebraic number, there is a rational integer r such that $r\theta$ is an algebraic integer.*

θ satisfies an equation

$$a_n x^n + a_{n-1}x^{n-1} + \cdots + a_0 = 0,$$

where the a_i are rational integers. Then $a_n\theta$ satisfies

$$x^n + a_{n-1}x^{n-1} + a_n a_{n-2}x^{n-2}$$
$$+ a_n^2 a_{n-3}x^{n-3} + \cdots + a_n^{n-1}a_0 = 0.$$

This makes it an algebraic integer.

An elegant treatment of these elementary properties of algebraic integers without the use of symmetric functions will be found in the two books of Landau listed in the bibliography.

2. **The integers in a quadratic field.** A *quadratic* field is a field of degree 2 over the rationals. Such a field is necessarily of the form $R(\theta)$, where θ is a root of a quadratic polynomial irreducible over the rationals. By Theorem 6.5 we can assume θ to be an algebraic integer; let it satisfy the equation $x^2 + 2ax + b = 0$, where a and b are rational numbers. Then $\theta = -a \pm \sqrt{a^2 - b}$. Remove from $a^2 - b$ all square factors, so that $a^2 - b = s^2D$, where D has no factor to higher than the first power. Clearly $R(\theta) = R(\sqrt{D})$. In summary, every quadratic field is of the form $R(\sqrt{D})$, where D is a rational integer free of square factors.

By Theorem 4.6 the numbers 1, $\sqrt{D}$ form a basis for the field $R(\sqrt{D})$, so that every number in it can be written in the form $\dfrac{l + m\sqrt{D}}{n}$, where l, m, n are rational integers. By cancelling, if necessary, we can assume that l, m and n are relatively prime, and that n is positive. We shall make this assumption.

How does one identify the algebraic integers among the elements of $R(\sqrt{D})$? The answer depends on the nature of the integer D. $\dfrac{l + m\sqrt{D}}{n}$ is an integer only if it satisfies a quadratic $x^2 + bx + c = 0$, where b and c are rational integers, so we may write

(6.1) $\quad (l + m\sqrt{D})^2 + bn(l + m\sqrt{D}) + cn^2 = 0.$

Then

(6.2) $\qquad\qquad l^2 + m^2D + bnl + cn^2 = 0$

and

$$m(2l + bn) = 0.$$

If $m = 0$ then $\dfrac{l + m\sqrt{D}}{n}$ is an integer if and only if $n|l$; we assume then that $m \neq 0$. In this case $-2l = bn$, so that equation (6.2) becomes

$$m^2D - l^2 + cn^2 = 0.$$

Let $(l, n) = d$. Then $d^2 \mid m^2D$. Since D is square-free, $d|m^2$. But l, m and n by assumption share no factor except 1. Hence $d = 1$, and l and n are relatively prime. But $bn = -2l$, so that $l \mid b$. Consequently $n = 1$ or 2.

If $n = 1$, then $\dfrac{l + m\sqrt{D}}{n}$ is necessarily an integer. This follows from the equation (6.1). The possibility $n = 2$ must be scrutinized more closely. The number $\dfrac{l + m\sqrt{D}}{2}$ satisfies the quadratic equation

$$x^2 - lx + \frac{l^2 - m^2D}{4} = 0.$$

Consequently it is an integer if and only if $\dfrac{l^2 - m^2D}{4}$ is a rational integer, that is

$$l^2 \equiv m^2D \ (4).$$

Since $(l, n) = (l, 2) = 1$, l must be odd, say $l = 2t + 1$.

Then $l^2 = 4t^2 + 4t + 1$, and the requirement becomes

(6.3) $1 \equiv m^2 D \ (4).$

Now D is congruent to 1, 2, or 3 modulo 4, since D is square free. We consider each of these three possibilities separately. If $D \equiv 1 \ (4)$, then (6.3) reduces to $1 \equiv m^2 (4)$. This holds if m is odd, but not if m is even. Hence if $D \equiv 1 \ (4)$ all numbers of the form $\dfrac{l + m \sqrt{D}}{2}$, l and m both odd, are integers. If $D \equiv 2 \ (4)$, then D is even, so (6.3) cannot hold for any choice of m. Finally, if $D \equiv 3 (4)$ the equation (6.3) becomes $1 \equiv 3 \ m^2 (4)$. If m is even this is impossible; if $m = 2s + 1$ is odd (6.3) reduces to the contradiction $1 \equiv 3(4)$. Consequently $n = 2$ yields no integers unless $D \equiv 1(4)$. We have established

THEOREM 6.6. *Every quadratic field is of the form* $R(\sqrt{D})$, *where D is a square-free rational integer. The algebraic integers consist of these classes:*

1. *all numbers of the form* $l + m \sqrt{D}$, *where l and m are rational integers, and*

2. *if $D \equiv 1(4)$, but not otherwise, all numbers of the form* $\dfrac{l + m \sqrt{D}}{2}$, *where l and m are odd.*

3. **Integral bases.** Let $K = R(\theta)$ be an algebraic number field of degree n. By virtue of Theorem 6.5 we may assume θ to be an integer and shall do so. By Theorem 4.6 every element of K can be written uniquely in the form $\sum_{i=0}^{n-1} a_i \theta^i$, where the a_i are in R.

A set of integers $\alpha_1, \cdots, \alpha_s$ is called an *integral basis* of K if every integer α in K can be written uniquely in the form

$$\alpha = b_1 \alpha_1 + \cdots + b_s \alpha_s,$$

where the b_i are rational integers. We shall show that an integral basis is necessarily a basis.

Let β be an element of K. By Theorem 6.5 $r\beta$ is an integer for a suitable choice of the rational integer r. Consequently we can write

$$r\beta = b_1\alpha_1 + \cdots + b_s\alpha_s,$$

$$\beta = \frac{b_1}{r}\alpha_1 + \cdots + \frac{b_s}{r}\alpha_s.$$

It remains only to show that the α_i are linearly independent over R. Suppose

$$c_1\alpha_1 + \cdots + c_s\alpha_s = 0,$$

where the c_i are rational numbers. By multiplying the equation by the greatest common denominator we find a relation

$$d_1\alpha_1 + \cdots + d_s\alpha_s = 0,$$

where the d_i are rational integers. By the definition of an integral basis the d_i are all zero. Consequently the c_i are all zero, and the α_i are linearly independent.

LEMMA 6.7. *An integral basis is a basis.*

It follows immediately that $s = n$, that is, that the number of elements in an integral basis equals the degree of the field.

LEMMA 6.8. *If $\alpha_1, \cdots, \alpha_n$ is any basis of K consisting only of integers, then $\Delta[\alpha_1, \cdots, \alpha_n]$ is a rational integer.*

The conjugates of the α_i are algebraic integers. Consequently

$$\Delta = \Delta[\alpha_1, \cdots, \alpha_n] = \begin{vmatrix} \alpha_1^{(1)} & \cdots & \alpha_n^{(1)} \\ \cdots\cdots\cdots\cdots \\ \alpha_1^{(n)} & \cdots & \alpha_n^{(n)} \end{vmatrix}^2$$

is an algebraic integer. By Theorem 5.11 with $F = R$, Δ is also a rational number. So it is a rational integer.

THEOREM 6.9. *Every algebraic number field has at least one integral basis.*

Let $K = R(\theta)$ be an algebraic number field, where θ is assumed to be integral. Consider all bases for K whose elements are algebraic integers; $1, \theta, \cdots, \theta^{n-1}$ is an example*. Since, by Lemma 6.8, the discriminant of each such basis is a rational integer, there is one basis, $\omega_1, \cdots, \omega_n$, for which $|\Delta(\omega_1, \cdots, \omega_n)|$ is a minimum d. By Theorem 5.11 d is not zero.

We shall prove that $\omega_1, \cdots, \omega_n$ is an integral basis. For suppose it were not. Since it is in any case a basis, there is an integer ω, such that

$$\omega = a_1\omega_1 + \cdots + a_n\omega_n,$$

where the a_i are rational numbers, but not all integers. We may suppose that a_1 is not integral. Write it as $a_1 = a + r$, where a is a rational integer and $0 < r < 1$. Define

$$\omega_1^* = \omega - a\omega_1 = (a_1 - a)\omega_1 + a_2\omega_2 + \cdots + a_n\omega_n,$$
$$\omega_i^* = \omega_i, \qquad\qquad i = 2, \cdots, n.$$

The determinant

$$\begin{vmatrix} a_1 - a & a_2 & a_3 & \cdots \\ 0 & 1 & 0 & \cdots \\ 0 & 0 & 1 & 0 \\ 0 & \cdots\cdots & & 1 \end{vmatrix} = a_1 - a = r$$

is not zero. By Theorem 5.4 $\omega_1^*, \cdots, \omega_n^*$ is a basis; moreover it consists entirely of integers. Also

$$\Delta[\omega_1^*, \cdots, \omega_n^*] = r^2\,\Delta[\omega_1, \cdots, \omega_n],$$
$$|\Delta[\omega_1^*, \cdots, \omega_n^*]| < |\Delta[\omega_1, \cdots, \omega_n]|$$

*We have not proved that $1, \theta, \cdots, \theta^{n-1}$ is an *integral* basis. That it need not be will become apparent later in the chapter.

contrary to the choice of the last expression as a minimum. For reasons which are now clear an integral basis is also called a *minimal* basis.

THEOREM 6.10. *All integral bases for a field* $K = R(\theta)$ *have the same discriminant.*

Let $\alpha_1, \cdots, \alpha_n; \beta_1, \cdots \beta_n$ be two integral bases. Then

$$\alpha_j = \sum_{i=1}^n c_{ij}\beta_i, \qquad j = 1, \cdots, n,$$

where the c_{ij} are rational integers. But

(6.4) $$\Delta[\alpha_1, \cdots, \alpha_n] = |c_{ij}|^2 \Delta[\beta_1, \cdots, \beta_n],$$

and $|c_{ij}|^2$ is a rational integer not zero, so that

$$\Delta[\beta_1, \cdots, \beta_n] \mid \Delta[\alpha_1, \cdots, \alpha_n].$$

By reversing the roles of the α_j and β_i we find that

$$\Delta[\alpha_1, \cdots \alpha_n] \mid \Delta[\beta_1, \cdots, \beta_n].$$

But the discriminants are rational integers, so that $\Delta[\alpha_1, \cdots, \alpha_n] = \pm\Delta[\beta_1, \cdots, \beta_n]$. By (6.4) the plus sign must prevail, and the proof is complete.

The discriminant d common to all integral bases is called the *discriminant of the field* K. Clearly $d \neq 0$. Since d is a rational integer, $|d| \geq 1$. Later it will be shown that if $K \neq R$, then $|d| > 1$.

4. **Examples of integral bases.** We begin by obtaining integral bases for the quadratic fields $R(\sqrt{D})$ discussed in §2.

First, if $D \not\equiv 1(4)$ then every integer is of the form $l + m \sqrt{D}$ (Theorem 6.6). Consequently an integral basis is $1, \sqrt{D}$. Note that in this case the discriminant of the field is

$$d = \begin{vmatrix} 1 & \sqrt{D} \\ 1 & -\sqrt{D} \end{vmatrix}^2 = 4D.$$

Next suppose that $D \equiv 1 \ (4)$. Every integer is of the form $\dfrac{l + m \sqrt{D}}{2}$ where l and m are both even or both odd. In particular $\dfrac{1 + \sqrt{D}}{2}$ is an integer. It follows that every integer can be written in the form

$$a + b \left(\frac{1 + \sqrt{D}}{2} \right),$$

where a and b are rational integers. An integral basis is therefore $1, \dfrac{1 + \sqrt{D}}{2}$. Moreover

$$d = \begin{vmatrix} 1 & \dfrac{1 + \sqrt{D}}{2} \\[2mm] 1 & \dfrac{1 - \sqrt{D}}{2} \end{vmatrix}^2 = D$$

THEOREM 6.11. *An integral basis for $R(\sqrt{D})$ is $1, \sqrt{D}$ if $D \not\equiv 1(4)$ and $1, \dfrac{1 + \sqrt{D}}{2}$ if $D \equiv 1 \ (4)$. In the former case $d = 4D$, in the latter $d = D$.*

A more complicated problem is the derivation of an integral basis for the cyclotomic field $R(\zeta)$, where ζ is a primitive p^{th} root of unity. It was shown in §4 of Chapter V that the set $1, \zeta, \cdots, \zeta^{p-2}$ is a basis for $R(\zeta)$. We shall now show that it is in fact an integral basis.

LEMMA 6.12. *If $\lambda = 1 - \zeta$, then $1, \lambda, \cdots, \lambda^{p-2}$ is an integral basis for $R(\zeta)$.*

Let $\omega_1, \cdots, \omega_{p-1}$ be some integral basis for $R(\zeta)$. Then

$$(6.5) \qquad \lambda^j = \sum_{i=1}^{p-1} c_{ij} \, \omega_i, \qquad j = 0, \cdots, p - 2,$$

where each c_{ij} is a rational integer. By (5.1)

(6.6) $\Delta[1, \lambda, \cdots, \lambda^{p-2}] = |c_{ij}|^2 \Delta[\omega_1, \cdots, \omega_{p-1}].$

Now

$$\lambda = 1 - \zeta$$
(6.7) $$\lambda^2 = 1 - 2\zeta + \zeta^2$$
$$\lambda^3 = 1 - 3\zeta + 3\zeta^2 - \zeta^3$$
$$\cdot \quad \cdot \quad \cdot$$

and also

$$\zeta = 1 - \lambda$$
$$\zeta^2 = 1 - 2\lambda + \lambda^2$$
$$\zeta^3 = 1 - 3\lambda + 3\lambda^2 - \lambda^3$$
$$\cdot \quad \cdot \quad \cdot \quad ,$$

so that

$$\Delta[1, \lambda, \cdots, \lambda^{p-2}] = |a_{ij}|^2 \Delta[1, \zeta, \cdots, \zeta^{p-2}]$$

and

$$\Delta[1, \zeta, \cdots, \zeta^{p-2}] = |a_{ij}|^2 \Delta[1, \lambda, \cdots, \lambda^{p-2}],$$

where the a_{ij} are simply the binomial coefficients appearing in (6.7). Hence $|a_{ij}|^2 = 1$, and so by (6.6)

$$\Delta[1, \zeta, \cdots, \zeta^{p-2}] = |c_{ij}|^2 \Delta[\omega_1, \cdots, \omega_{p-1}].$$

Since $|c_{ij}|^2$ and $\Delta[\omega_1, \cdots, \omega_{p-1}]$ are rational integers, it follows from Theorem 5.12 that $|c_{ij}| = \pm p^j$ for some integer $j \geq 0$.

If we solve the system (6.5) for the ω_i it turns out that they can be expressed in the form

$$\frac{a_0 + a_1 \lambda + \cdots + a_{p-2} \lambda^{p-2}}{p^j},$$

where the a_i are rational integers. Since $\omega_1, \cdots, \omega_{p-1}$ is an integral basis, it follows that every integer in $R(\zeta)$ can be expressed in this form.

If $1, \lambda, \cdots, \lambda^{p-2}$ is *not* an integral basis there must therefore be an integer in $R(\zeta)$ of the form

$$\frac{a_0 + a_1\lambda + \cdots + a_{p-2}\lambda^{p-2}}{p}$$

where p does not divide $a_0 + a_1\lambda + \cdots + a_{p-2}\lambda^{p-2}$. Let a_m be the a_i with least subscript such that $p \nmid a_m$. Then

$$\frac{a_m\lambda^m + \cdots + a_{p-2}\lambda^{p-2}}{p}$$

is an algebraic integer, where $m \leq p - 2$.

As we showed in §4 of Chapter V,

$$\begin{aligned}
p &= (1 - \zeta)(1 - \zeta^2) \cdots (1 - \zeta^{p-1}) \\
&= (1 - \zeta)(1 - \zeta) \cdots (1 - \zeta)\kappa \\
&= \lambda^{p-1}\kappa = \lambda^{m+1}\kappa',
\end{aligned}$$

where κ and κ' are algebraic integers. Hence

$$\frac{a_m\lambda^m + \cdots + a_{p-2}\lambda^{p-2}}{\lambda^{m+1}}$$

is an algebraic integer. λ^{m+1} cancels into all terms but the first, so we can remove them to conclude that a_m/λ is an algebraic integer. We write $a_m = a$ for simplicity.

We shall prove that a/λ cannot be an algebraic integer, thus arriving at a contradiction. From this it will follow that $1, \lambda, \cdots, \lambda^{p-2}$ is an integral basis. Let $x = a/\lambda = a/(1 - \zeta)$. Then $\zeta = 1 - \dfrac{a}{x}$, so $1 = \left(1 - \dfrac{a}{x}\right)^p$, $x^p = (x - a)^p$. Hence a/λ satisfies an equation

$$g(x) = px^{p-1} + p(\cdots) + a^{p-1} = 0,$$

where $p \nmid a$. Since $p \nmid a$, the polynomial $x^{p-1} g\left(\dfrac{1}{x}\right) = a^{p-1} x^{p-1}$.
$+ \ p(\cdots) \ + \ p$ is irreducible by Eisenstein's criterion.
Hence $g(x)$ is irreducible over R. Since it is primitive and
its leading coefficient is not 1, its root a/λ is not an algebraic
integer. This proves the lemma.

Since $1, \lambda, \cdots, \lambda^{p-2}$ is an integral basis, so is $1, \zeta, \cdots,$
ζ^{p-2} in view of the relation (6.7). Combining this fact
with Theorem 5.12 we arrive at

THEOREM 6.13. *The set* $1, \zeta, \cdots, \zeta^{p-2}$ *is an integral basis
for* $R(\zeta)$. *This field has discriminant* $(-1)^{(p-1)/2} p^{p-2}$.

CHAPTER VII

ARITHMETIC IN ALGEBRAIC NUMBER FIELDS

1. Units and primes. Consider the ring of *all* algebraic integers, and let us try to model a theory of factorization in this ring after the pattern of Chapter I. We might say that α *divides* β, written $\alpha \mid \beta$, if β/α is an algebraic integer. ϵ is a *unit* if ϵ divides 1. α is a *prime* if it is not zero or a unit, and if any factorization $\alpha = \beta\gamma$ into integers implies that either β or γ is a unit.

This attempt, natural in view of our earlier work, is unfortunately doomed to failure because there are no primes in the ring of all algebraic integers! For let α be an integer different from zero or a unit. Then we can always write $\alpha = \sqrt{\alpha}\,\sqrt{\alpha}$. If α satisfies $p(x) = 0$, then $\sqrt{\alpha}$ satisfies $p(x^2) = 0$, so $\sqrt{\alpha}$ is an integer. This forces us to abandon the definitions just given.

Instead, let us confine our attention to the ring of all integers in a *fixed* algebraic number field $K = R(\theta)$. This is in fact what we did in Chapter I. The definitions given above will now have to be altered. α *divides* β, $\alpha \mid \beta$, if β/α is an integer of K. ϵ is a *unit* if $\epsilon \mid 1$. α is a *prime* if it is not zero or a unit, and if any factorization $\alpha = \beta\gamma$ into integers of K implies that either β or γ is a unit.

With these definitions factorization of integers in K into the product of primes is always possible. This we shall verify immediately. On the other hand, as we saw in Chapter I, the ring H of all integers* in $R(\sqrt{-5})$ does not have the property of *unique* factorization. Before investigating the cause of this phenomenon and the

---

* That H actually constitutes the ring of all integers in $R(\sqrt{-5})$ follows from Theorem 6.6, since $-5 \not\equiv 1(4)$.

method for remedying it, we shall prove that in K factorization into primes is possible, whether or not it is unique.

If α is an integer in K and K is of degree n over R, then α has n conjugates $\alpha_1, \cdots, \alpha_n$ for K. We define the *norm* of α, written $N(\alpha)$ or $N\alpha$, by

$$N\alpha = \alpha_1 \cdots \alpha_n.$$

LEMMA 7.1. *$N\alpha$ is a rational integer.*

Let $f(x)$ be the field polynomial of α (as defined in the proof of Theorem 5.10). Since $f(x)$ is a power of the minimal polynomial it has integral coefficients. Hence

$$f(x) = x^n + a_{n-1}x^{n-1} + \cdots + a_0$$
$$= (x - \alpha_1)(x - \alpha_2) \cdots (x - \alpha_n),$$

where a_0 is a rational integer. Then

$$N\alpha = \alpha_1 \cdots \alpha_n = (-1)^n a_0$$

LEMMA 7.2. *$N(\alpha\beta) = N\alpha \cdot N\beta$.*

If $\alpha_1, \alpha_2, \cdots, \alpha_n; \beta_1, \beta_2, \cdots, \beta_n$ are the conjugates of α and β respectively for K, then $\alpha_1\beta_1, \alpha_2\beta_2, \cdots, \alpha_n\beta_n$ are the conjugates of $\alpha\beta$ for K. This implies the lemma.

LEMMA 7.3. *α is a unit in K if and only if $N\alpha = \pm 1$.*

For α is a unit if and only if $\alpha \mid 1$. If $\alpha \mid 1$ then $N\alpha \mid 1$, $N\alpha = \pm 1$. If $N\alpha = \pm 1$, then $\alpha_1, \cdots, \alpha_n \mid 1$, and so $\alpha \mid 1$.

THEOREM 7.4. *If $N\alpha$ is a rational prime, α is prime in K.*

For if $\alpha = \beta\gamma$, $N\alpha = N\beta N\gamma$. Since $N\alpha$ is prime, one of $N\beta$ and $N\gamma$ is ± 1. Hence, by the preceding lemma, one of β and γ is a unit.

THEOREM 7.5. *Every integer in K, not zero or a unit, can be factored into the product of primes.*

If α is not already prime write $\alpha = \beta\gamma$, where neither β nor γ is a unit. Repeat the procedure for β and γ, and continue in this way. It must stop, for otherwise $\alpha = \gamma_1 \cdots \gamma_n$ where n is arbitrarily large, and then $|N\alpha| = |N\gamma_1| \cdots |N\gamma_n|$ can be made as large as one pleases, since each factor $|N\gamma_i|$ exceeds unity.

COROLLARY 7.6. *There are an infinite number of primes in an algebraic field.*

The same argument used in §1 of Chapter II shows that there is an infinite number of primes in K if there is at least one. But there is at least one. For the number 2 certainly belongs to K, and by Theorem 7.5 it has a prime factor.

We shall resume the question of uniqueness of fac torization in §3.

2. **Units in a quadratic field.** To illustrate some of the material of the preceding section we shall discuss the problem of determining the units in a quadratic field $R(\sqrt{D})$. If $\alpha = a + b\sqrt{D}$ is an integer in $R(\sqrt{D})$, then

$$N\alpha = (a + b\sqrt{D})(a - b\sqrt{D}) = a^2 - Db^2.$$

This reduces the problem of determining the units to the solution of the equation $a^2 - Db^2 = \pm 1$.

If $D \not\equiv 1 \ (4)$ the integers are all the numbers of the form $l + m\sqrt{D}$, where l and m are rational integers. Then to determine the units we must solve

$$(7.1) \qquad l^2 - Dm^2 = \pm 1$$

for rational integers l, m.

If $D \equiv 1(4)$ there are in addition to these the integers $\dfrac{l + m\sqrt{D}}{2}$ where l and m are both odd. Then all further units come from the solution of

$$(7.2) \qquad l^2 - Dm^2 = \pm 4$$

in odd integers l, m.

Suppose first that $D < 0$. In this case the field $R(\sqrt{D})$ is called imaginary. Note that the left-hand members of both (7.1) and (7.2) become positive, so the minus signs in the right-hand members must be dropped. Then the units are obtained from $l^2 - Dm^2 = 1$ and, if $D \equiv 1(4)$, also from $l^2 - Dm^2 = 4$. Since $-D > 0$, each of these equations can have at most a finite number of solutions. We shall determine them explicitly, first stopping to remind the reader that D is square-free.

If $D < -1$, then $l^2 - Dm^2 = 1$ has only the solutions $l = \pm 1$, $m = 0$; if $D < -4$, $l^2 - Dm^2 = 4$ also has only these solutions. Hence if $D < -4$ the only units are ± 1. It remains to consider the cases $D = -1, -2, -3$. The first of these corresponds to the field $R(i)$, and we have already proved in Chapter I that the units in this field are $\pm 1, \pm i$. Secondly, since $D = -2 \not\equiv 1(4)$ the initial remark of this paragraph shows that the only units in $R(\sqrt{-2})$ are ± 1.

We turn our attention to $R(\sqrt{-3})$. Since $-3 \equiv 1(4)$ we can expect in addition to ± 1 further units arising from the solution of $l^2 + 3m^2 = 4$. This has solutions $(1, 1)$, $(1, -1)$, $(-1, 1)$, $(-1, -1)$. So the units in $R(\sqrt{-3})$ are $\pm 1, \dfrac{1 \pm \sqrt{-3}}{2}, \dfrac{-1 \pm \sqrt{-3}}{2}$. Note that they are the roots of $x \pm 1$ and $x^2 \pm x + 1$.

THEOREM 7.7. *The quadratic field* $R(\sqrt{D})$ *where* D *is negative and square-free, has only the units* ± 1 *unless* $D = -1$, *in which case there are the additional units* $\pm i$. *or unless* $D = -3$ *in which case there are the additional units*

$$\frac{1 \pm \sqrt{-3}}{2}, \qquad \frac{-1 \pm \sqrt{-3}}{2}.$$

But what if $D > 0$, so that the field is real? The situation becomes more complicated than in the imaginary case, and we shall content ourselves for the present with a solution for the case $D = 2$. Since $2 \not\equiv 1(4)$ only the solutions of (7.1)—that is, $l^2 - 2m^2 = \pm 1$—concern us.

LEMMA 7.8. $R(\sqrt{2})$ *has no unit between* 1 *and* $1 + \sqrt{2}$.

For suppose that $\epsilon = x + y\sqrt{2}$, where $x^2 - 2y^2 = \pm 1$, lies between 1 and $1 + \sqrt{2}$. Then $1 < \epsilon < 1 + \sqrt{2}$ and since $x - y\sqrt{2} = \pm \dfrac{1}{x + y\sqrt{2}}$, $-1 < x - y\sqrt{2} < 1$. Adding these inequalities we get $0 < 2x < 2 + \sqrt{2}$, $0 < x < 1.8$. Since x is an integer, $x = 1$. But then $1 < 1 + y\sqrt{2} < 1 + \sqrt{2}$, which is not possible for any integer y.

Observe that one solution of $l^2 - 2m^2 = \pm 1$ is $(1, 1)$, so that $\lambda = 1 + \sqrt{2}$ is a unit.

THEOREM 7.9. $R(\sqrt{2})$ *has an infinite number of units. They are given by* $\pm\lambda^n$, $n = 0, \pm 1, \pm 2, \cdots$.

To prove this note first that all the elements of $R(\sqrt{2})$ are real. Hence if ϵ is a unit in $R(\sqrt{2})$ it is positive or negative.

Suppose $\epsilon > 0$. Since $\lambda = 1 + \sqrt{2}$ exceeds 1 we can find an integer n such that $\lambda^n \leq \epsilon < \lambda^{n+1}$. If $\lambda^n < \epsilon < \lambda^{n+1}$ then $1 < \epsilon\lambda^{-n} < 1 + \sqrt{2}$. But $N(\epsilon\lambda^{-n}) = N(\epsilon)/N(\lambda)^n = 1$ since ϵ and λ are units. Then $\epsilon\lambda^{-n}$ is a unit between 1 and $1 + \sqrt{2}$, contrary to Lemma 7.8 The only alternative is $\epsilon = \lambda^n$. Since $1/\epsilon$ and $-\epsilon$ are also units, the proof is complete.

In a later Chapter on units we shall show that every algebraic number field except R and the fields of Theorem 7.7 has an infinite number of units, so that $R(\sqrt{2})$ is more typical of the general case than the imaginary quadratic fields. The proof must be postponed as too difficult at this stage.

3. **The uniqueness of factorization*.** It has already been observed that Theorem 7.5 says nothing about uniqueness (that is, to within order and units) of factorization into primes. In order to understand how the failure of uniqueness can come about, let us examine closely the integers in $R(\sqrt{-5})$. As we have seen in Chapter I,

$$21 = 3\cdot7 = (1 + 2\sqrt{-5})(1 - 2\sqrt{-5}),$$

where all the factors which appear are primes. We then have the following situation: the number 3, a prime, divides $(1 + 2\sqrt{-5})(1 - 2\sqrt{-5})$, but fails to divide either factor in $R(\sqrt{-5})$. That this circumstance cannot come to pass in R or $R(i)$ was already proved in Chapter I.

In order to explain this situation we restore temporarily the definition of division given at the beginning of §1, but which was subsequently abandoned. Let $\alpha = 1 + 2\sqrt{-5}, \lambda = 2 + \sqrt{-5}$. Then

$$\frac{\alpha^2}{\lambda} = -2 + 3\sqrt{-5}, \qquad \frac{9}{\lambda} = 2 - \sqrt{-5}$$

are integers of $R(\sqrt{-5})$ It follows that their square roots $\frac{\alpha}{\sqrt{\lambda}}, \frac{3}{\sqrt{\lambda}}$ are integers, but these integers are not in $R(\sqrt{-5})$ (why?). In other words 3 and $1 + 2\sqrt{-5}$ are both divisible (in the extended sense of "division") by an integer $\sqrt{\lambda}$ which is not in $R(\sqrt{-5})$. Moreover, since

$$\sqrt{\lambda} = \left(-\frac{2\alpha}{\sqrt{\lambda}}\right)\alpha - \left(\frac{12 - 3\sqrt{-5}}{\sqrt{\lambda}}\right)3,$$

any other factor common to 3 and $\alpha = 1 + 2\sqrt{-5}$ divides $\sqrt{\lambda}$.

* The material of this section is adapted from Chapter V of Hecke's book listed in the bibliography.

Similarly 7 and $1 - 2\sqrt{-5}$ have the "highest common factor" $\sqrt{\kappa}$, where $\kappa = 2 + 3\sqrt{-5}$.

A simple computation shows that

$$1 + 2\sqrt{-5} = \sqrt{\lambda}\,\sqrt{-\bar{\kappa}} \qquad 3 = \sqrt{\lambda}\,\sqrt{\bar{\lambda}}$$

$$1 - 2\sqrt{-5} = \sqrt{\bar{\lambda}}\,\sqrt{-\kappa} \qquad 7 = \sqrt{\kappa}\,\sqrt{\bar{\kappa}}$$

where the bar denotes the complex-conjugate. Then 21 can be factored, but not in $R(\sqrt{-5})$, as

$$21 = \sqrt{\lambda}\,\sqrt{\bar{\lambda}}\,\sqrt{-\kappa}\,\sqrt{-\bar{\kappa}},$$

and the various factorizations obtained in $R(\sqrt{-5})$ come from pairing these four factors in different ways.

In summary:

1. Prime numbers in $R(\sqrt{-5})$ which are not associated (that is, whose ratio is not a unit) can have a common factor which is not in $R(\sqrt{-5})$.

2. The totality of integers in $R(\sqrt{-5})$ which are divisible by a prime number α in $R(\sqrt{-5})$ need not coincide with the totality of integers in $R(\sqrt{-5})$ which are divisible by a factor of α not in $R(\sqrt{-5})$ and not a unit. ($\alpha = 1 + 2\sqrt{-5}$ is prime and $\sqrt{\lambda}$ divides both α and 3 but 3 is not divisible by α).

It appears then that in an algebraic number field K the primes are not necessarily the atoms from which all the integers are constructed. In $R(\sqrt{-5})$, for example it seems to be necessary to enlarge the ring of integers to include such "ideal" numbers as $\sqrt{\lambda}$, $\sqrt{\bar{\kappa}}$ which do not originally belong to it. But how shall we characterize those numbers which must be added to K?

Suppose an integer ξ is a possible candidate for admission to K by virtue of being a common factor to two integers relatively prime in K. Consider the *totality A of all integers in K which are divisible by* ξ (in the extended sense). It has the following property: if α and β are integers in A, so are all integers in K of the form $\lambda\alpha + \mu\beta$, where λ and μ are also integers in K. Any set of integers in K with the latter property we call an *ideal*.

This suggests the following procedure for answering the question raised above. Let us consider any ideal in K and try to prove that it is identical with the totality of integers in K which are divisible by some fixed integer ξ not necessarily in K. If we can accomplish this and can show further that ξ is in some sense unique, then we have characterized the missing integers by means of the ideals. This is the attack we shall pursue in the succeeding chapter.

But this poses another problem. If we are going to make ideals a substitute for integers, then the problem of factorization of integers is shifted to that of factorization of ideals. As we shall see, there is a completely satisfactory arithmetic for ideals, and by means of it we shall finally settle the problem of unique factorization.

4. **Ideals in an algebraic number field.** Let K be an algebraic number field. A set A of integers in K is an *ideal* if, together with any pair of integers α and β in A, the set also contains $\lambda\alpha + \mu\beta$ for any integers λ and μ in K. A set of integers $\omega_1, \cdots, \omega_r$ in A is said to form a *basis* for A if every element α of A can be uniquely represented in the form

$$(7.3) \qquad \alpha = c_1\omega_1 + \cdots + c_r\omega_r ,$$

where the c_i are rational integers.

Let us denote by (0) the ideal consisting of 0 alone. We shall show that if an ideal $A \neq (0)$ in a field K has a basis $\omega_1, \cdots, \omega_r$, then r must equal n, the degree of the field. By virtue of the uniqueness of the representation (7.3) the set $\omega_1, \cdots, \omega_r$ must be linearly independent over

R. Hence $r \leq n$, by Lemma 5.1. To show that $r < n$ is impossible, let $\beta_1, \cdots, \beta_n$ be an integral basis for K over R. If α is an element of A different from zero, then $\alpha\beta_1, \cdots, \alpha\beta_n$ are linearly independent and belong to A. On account of their linear independence they form a basis for K. Moreover

$$\alpha\beta_j = \sum_{i=1}^{n} a_{ij}\,\omega_i, \qquad j = 1, \cdots, n,$$

where we define ω_i to be zero for $r < i \leq n$. Then

$$\Delta[\alpha\beta_1, \cdots, \alpha\beta_n] = |\,a_{ij}\,|^2 \Delta[\omega_1, \cdots, \omega_n].$$

But $\Delta[\omega_1, \cdots, \omega_n] = \Delta[\omega_1, \cdots, \omega_r, 0, \cdots] = 0$. Hence $\Delta[\alpha\beta_1, \cdots, \alpha\beta_n] = 0$, in contradiction to the fact that the discriminant of a basis is never zero. It follows that $r = n$.

To prove that an ideal $A \neq (0)$ necessarily has a basis we can imitate the proof of Theorem 6.9. Consider all sets $\alpha_1, \cdots, \alpha_n$ of integers in A which form a basis for K; the numbers $\alpha\beta_1, \cdots, \alpha\beta_n$ which occur above furnish an example. By Lemma 6.8, $\Delta[\alpha_1, \cdots, \alpha_n]$ is always a rational integer not zero, so we can pick such a set $\omega_1, \cdots, \omega_n$ from A for which $|\,\Delta[\omega_1, \cdots, \omega_n]\,|$ is a minimum. This is a basis for the ideal A, by precisely the same argument as that used to prove Theorem 6.9.

Conversely, every integer in K of the form (7.3) is in A. This is a consequence of the definition of an ideal and the fact that all rational integers are integers in K. Thus we have proved

THEOREM 7.10. *If K is of degree n over R and $A \neq (0)$ is an ideal in K, then there exist integers $\omega_1, \cdots, \omega_n$ in A such that A is the totality of integers of the form $\sum_{i=1}^{n} c_i\omega_i$, the c_i being rational integers.*

An ideal A is said to be *generated* by $\alpha_1, \cdots, \alpha_t$, written $A = (\alpha_1, \cdots, \alpha_t)$, if A consists of all sums $\sum_{i=1}^{t} \lambda_i\alpha_i$, where the λ_i are integers, *not* necessarily rational, in K. Obviously if $\omega_1, \cdots, \omega_n$ is a basis for A, then $A = (\omega_1, \cdots, \omega_n)$; but if $A = (\alpha_1, \cdots, \alpha_t)$, the α_i do not necessarily form a basis for A. For example, consider the ideal (2) in $R(i)$. This ideal consists of all integers of the form $2a + 2bi$, where a and b are rational integers; so a basis for (2) is $2, 2i$. The number 2 alone is not a basis for (2).

An ideal A is *principal* if it is generated by a single integer—that is, $A = (\alpha)$.

THEOREM 7.11. *Every ideal in R or in $R(i)$ is principal. There is an ideal in $R(\sqrt{-5})$ which is not principal.*

First, let A be an ideal in R. A consists entirely of rational integers. Suppose $A \neq (0)$; then it contains an element $a \neq 0$. In addition it contains $a - a = 0$ and $0 - a = -a$. So both $\pm a$ belong to A, and one of these must be positive. Hence A contains positive integers. Let m be the least positive integer in A. If n is any other number in A we can find q and r such that

$$n = mq + r, \qquad 0 \leq r < m.$$

But every number $ns + mt$ is in A, and $r = n - mq$ in particular. Then $0 < r < m$ is impossible, by the choice of m as the least positive integer in A. Hence $r = 0$ and $n = mq$. In other words, every element of A is a multiple of m. Moreover, every multiple of m is in A, so $A = (m)$, as required.

A similar argument applies to the ideals A in $R(i)$; but instead of choosing the least positive number in A, we take the element of least positive norm, and apply Theorem 1.6.

On the other hand the ideal $B = (3, 1 + 2\sqrt{-5})$ is not principal in $R(\sqrt{-5})$. For if $B = (\beta)$, then $\beta \mid 3$ $\beta \mid (1 + 2\sqrt{-5})$. Since 3 and $1 + 2\sqrt{-5}$ are both prime in $R(\sqrt{-5})$ and hence relatively prime, β must be a unit. The only units in $R(\sqrt{-5})$ are ± 1, so $B = (1)$ By the results of the preceding section every element of B is divisible by $\sqrt{\lambda}$ (in the extended sense of division) since 3 and $1 + 2\sqrt{-5}$ are so divisible. Hence $1/\sqrt{\lambda}$ is an integer, so that

$$\frac{1}{\lambda} = \frac{1}{2 + \sqrt{-5}} = \frac{2 - \sqrt{-5}}{9}$$

is an integer, in contradiction to Theorem 6.6. It follows that B cannot be principal in $R(\sqrt{-5})$.

The reader may suspect from this last theorem that unique factorization of integers in an algebraic number fields is equivalent to the principality of all ideals in it. This conjecture will be confirmed in Chapter IX.

CHAPTER VIII

THE FUNDAMENTAL THEOREM OF IDEAL THEORY

1. **Basic properties of ideals.** According to the last chapter, every ideal in the algebraic number field K can be written $A = (\alpha_1, \cdots, \alpha_s)$. Under what circumstances can we say that A and $B = (\beta_1, \cdots, \beta_t)$ are the same ideal? The simple answer is given by

THEOREM 8.1. *The ideals A and B are the same if and only if each α_i can be written as*

$$\alpha_i = \sum_j \gamma_{ij} \beta_j$$

and each β_j as

$$\beta_j = \sum_i \delta_{ji} \alpha_i,$$

where the γ_{ij}, δ_{ji} are integers of K.

The necessity of the condition is obvious. To prove the sufficiency let $\beta = \sum_j \lambda_j \beta_j$ be any element of B. Then $\beta = \sum_j \lambda_j \sum_i \delta_{ji} \alpha_i = \sum_i (\sum_j \lambda_j \delta_{ji}) \alpha_i$, so that β is in A. Similarly every element of A is in B. Hence $A = B$.

Two integers α and β in K are *associated* if α/β is a unit in K.

COROLLARY 8.2. *Two principal ideals (α) and (β) are the same if and only if α and β are associated.*

If α and β are associated, $\alpha = \beta\epsilon$, where ϵ is a unit, and $\beta = \alpha\left(\dfrac{1}{\epsilon}\right)$, where $1/\epsilon$ is a unit. By the preceding theorem, $(\alpha) = (\beta)$. Conversely if $(\alpha) = (\beta)$ then $\alpha = \beta\gamma$, $\beta = \alpha\delta$, where γ and δ are integers in K. Hence $\alpha = (\alpha\delta)\gamma$, $1 = \delta\gamma$, so that $N\gamma \mid 1$ and $\alpha/\beta = \gamma$ is a unit.

By the *product* AB of the ideals $A = (\alpha_1, \cdots, \alpha_s)$ and $B = (\beta_1, \cdots, \beta_t)$ in K we mean the ideal

$$AB = (\alpha_1\beta_1, \cdots, \alpha_i\beta_j, \cdots, \alpha_s\beta_t)$$

in K generated by all products $\alpha_i\beta_j$. It is easily verified by means of Theorem 8.1 that the product AB is independent of the particular sets of generators chosen for the ideals A and B. It is a direct consequence of the definition of product that for any ideals A, B and C,

$$AB = BA$$
$$(AB)C = A(BC).$$

We shall say that A *divides* B, written $A \mid B$, if an ideal C exists so that $B = AC$. A is then called a *factor* of B. A *includes* B, written $A \supset B$, if every element of B is contained in A. A is then called a *divisor* of B. Note very carefully this distinction we are making between a factor and a divisor.

LEMMA 8.3. *If $A \mid B$ then $A \supset B$.*

In other words, a factor is a divisor. For suppose that $B = AC$, where $C = (\gamma_1, \cdots, \gamma_v)$. Then $(\beta_1, \cdots, \beta_t) = (\alpha_1\gamma_1, \cdots, \alpha_i\gamma_j, \cdots, \alpha_s\gamma_v)$, so every β_k is of the form $\sum_{i,j}\lambda_{ij}\alpha_i\gamma_j = \sum_i (\sum_j\lambda_{ij}\gamma_j)\alpha_i$ and is contained in A. Hence A includes B.

LEMMA 8.4. *A rational integer not zero belongs to at most a finite number of ideals in K.*

Let $\omega_1, \cdots, \omega_n$ be an integral basis for K. Then every integer of the field is of the form $\alpha = \sum_{i=1}^{n}c_i\omega_i$, where the c_i are rational integers.

Suppose a is a rational integer not zero and A an ideal containing it. Since $\pm a$ are both in A we can assume that $a > 0$. Each c_i can be written

$$c_i = q_ia + r_i, \qquad 0 \leq r_i < a, 1 \leq i \leq n.$$

Then

$$\alpha = \sum (q_i a + r_i)\omega_i = a \sum q_i \omega_i + \sum r_i \omega_i = a\gamma + \beta,$$

where γ is an integer and β can take on only a finite number of different values (since $0 \leq r_i < a$).

Let $A = (\alpha_1, \cdots, \alpha_s)$. Since $a \epsilon A$, $A = (\alpha_1, \cdots, \alpha_s, a)$. Each α_i is of the form $a\gamma_i + \beta_i$ by the preceding remarks, so that $A = (a\gamma_1 + \beta_1, \cdots, a\gamma_s + \beta_s, a)$. By Theorem 8.1, $A = (\beta_1, \cdots, \beta_s)$. But β_i can take on only a finite number of different values for each $i = 1, \cdots, s$. So A can be one of only a finite number of ideals.

THEOREM 8.5. *An ideal* $A \neq (0)$ *has only a finite number of divisors.*

Let α be an element of A. Then $N\alpha = \alpha(\alpha_2 \cdots \alpha_n)$ is in A. If $B \supset A$, then $N\alpha$ is in B. But $N\alpha$ can belong to only a finite number of ideals B, by the preceding lemma.

From Lemma 8.3 we have also the

COROLLARY 8.6. *An ideal* $A \neq (0)$ *has only a finite number of factors.*

It is our purpose to establish a theory of unique factorization for ideals similar to that obtained in Chapter I for the rational integers. The role of the units in the latter theory will be assumed by the ideal (1)—that is, the ring of all integers in K. The ideals which take over the function of the prime rational integers are naturally those ideals P which have no factors except P and (1). It is customary in the classical literature to call such ideals "prime", but in modern ring theory the word "prime" is reserved for another property of ideals which will be mentioned subsequently; so for the present we shall use instead the word "irreducible". Then an ideal P is *irreducible* if it has no factors except P and (1). What we shall eventually prove is that every ideal in K different from (0) and (1) can be represented as the product of irreducible ideals, uniquely to within order and to within multiplication by (1).

We shall give two proofs of this important theorem: a modification of a classical proof based on ideas of A. Hurwitz and a modern proof due to E. Noether and W. Krull. These two proofs will be given in the following two sections, which can be read independently of one another.

It is useful to introduce two further kinds of ideals which will eventually turn out to be equivalent to one another and to irreducible ideals. An ideal A is *maximal* if it has no divisors except (1) and A—that is, if it is included in no larger ideal except (1). An ideal P different from (0) or (1) is *prime* if it has the following property: *whenever a product of integers $\gamma\delta$ is in P, so is either γ or δ.*

THEOREM 8.7. *An ideal P different from (0) or (1) is maximal if and only if it is prime.*

First suppose that $P = (\alpha_1, \cdots, \alpha_s)$ is maximal and let it contain $\gamma\delta$. If it contains γ we are through. Suppose i :does not contain γ; we shall show it contains δ. Let $P' = (\alpha_1, \cdots, \alpha_s, \gamma)$. Then $P' \supset P$. But P is maximal, so $P' = P$ or $P' = (1)$. $P' = P$ is impossible, for then γ belongs to P. Hence $P' = (1)$, so that 1 is contained in P'. 1 can therefore be written in the form

$$1 = \lambda_1\alpha_1 + \cdots + \lambda_s\alpha_s + \lambda\gamma,$$

so that

$$\delta = (\lambda_1\delta)\alpha_1 + \cdots + (\lambda_s\delta)\alpha_s + \lambda(\gamma\delta).$$

Since $\alpha_1, \cdots, \alpha_s$ and $\gamma\delta$ are in P, so is δ. Hence P is prime.

Conversely, let $P = (\alpha_1, \cdots, \alpha_s)$ be a prime ideal. Let $P' \supset P$, $P' \neq P$. We must show that $P' = (1)$. Let α be an integer in P' but not in P. Form its powers α^j; they are in P'.

Let $\omega_1, \cdots, \omega_n$ be an integral basis for K. Let $\beta \neq 0$ be any integer in P. Then $\pm N\beta$ are in P, so that P contains a positive rational integer a. According to the proof of Lemma 8.4 each integer in K can be written in the form $a\gamma + \sum_{i=1}^{n} r_i\omega_i$, where each of the r_i can take on only a finite number of different values. In particular each α^j is of the form

$$\alpha^j = a\gamma_j + \sum_{i=1}^{n} r_{ij}\omega_i.$$

Then $\alpha^j - a\gamma_j$ can take on only a finite number of different values. So there is a pair of integers k, l, $k > l$, such that

$$\alpha^k - a\gamma_k = \alpha^l - a\gamma_l.$$

$\alpha^k - \alpha^l = a(\gamma_k - \gamma_l)$ is in P, by the choice of a. Then $\alpha^l(\alpha^{k-l} - 1)$ is in P. Since P is a prime ideal, one of the two factors α^l and $\alpha^{k-l} - 1$ must be in P.

Now $\alpha^l = \alpha \cdot \alpha \cdots \alpha$ cannot be in P, for otherwise one of the factors α would be, and α was chosen as an integer not in P. Hence $\alpha^{k-l} - 1$ is in P. Since $P' \supset P$, $\alpha^{k-l} - 1$ is in P'. But every power of α is in P', α^{k-l} in particular. Hence -1 belongs to P', so that $P' = (1)$. It follows that P is maximal.

COROLLARY 8.8. *If P is a maximal ideal and $P \supset AB$, then $P \supset A$ or $P \supset B$.*

If $P \supset A$ we are done. Suppose α is in A but does not belong to P. If β is in B then $\alpha\beta$ is in P, for $P \supset AB$. But P is prime, according to Theorem 8.7, so that P contains β. Hence every element of B is contained in P, $P \supset B$.

2. The classical proof of the unique factorization theorem.

We begin with the following lemma.

LEMMA 8.9. *Every ideal A different from (0) and (1) has a maximal divisor.*

By Theorem 8.5 the ideal A has only a finite number of divisors. Any divisor B of A, $B \neq A$, has fewer divisors than A, for any divisor of B is a divisor of A, since $B \supset A$, and moreover A has a divisor which B does not, namely A itself.

Among the divisors of A choose one different from (1) with the smallest number of divisors. This is possible, by Theorem 8.5. Call it P. Then P is maximal. If it were not, then there would be an ideal $P' \neq (1)$ such that $P' \supset P$, $P' \neq P$. But then P' has fewer divisors than P, and $P' \supset A$, contrary to the choice of P.

The following lemmas will be used to establish the converse of Lemma 8.3.

LEMMA 8.10. *If*

$$f(x) = \delta_m x^m + \delta_{m-1} x^{m-1} + \cdots + \delta_0 \quad (\delta_m \neq 0)$$

is a polynomial with all its coefficients algebraic integers and ρ is one of its roots, then all the coefficients of the polynomial $f(x)/x - \rho$ are algebraic integers.

By Theorem 6.4, $\delta_m \rho$ is an algebraic integer, for it satisfies the equation

$$x^m + \delta_{m-1} x^{m-1} + \cdots + \delta_m{}^{m-1} \delta_0 = 0.$$

The lemma is certainly true if $m = 1$. Suppose it has been established for all polynomials of degree $\leq m - 1$. Since

$$\phi(x) = f(x) - \delta_m x^{m-1}(x - \rho)$$

is of degree $\leq m - 1$, and since $\phi(\rho) = 0$, the polynomial

$$\frac{\phi(x)}{x - \rho} = \frac{f(x)}{x - \rho} - \delta_m x^{m-1}$$

has integral coefficients. Then so has $f(x)/x - \rho$. This completes the induction.

LEMMA 8.11. *If $f(x)$ is the polynomial of Lemma* 8.10 *and*

$$f(x) = \delta_m(x - \rho_1) \cdots (x - \rho_m),$$

then $\delta_m\rho_1 \cdots \rho_k$ is an algebraic integer for $k = 1, 2, \cdots m$.

For by successive applications of the preceding lemma,

$$\frac{f(x)}{(x - \rho_{k+1}) \cdots (x - \rho_m)} = \delta_m(x - \rho_1) \cdots (x - \rho_k)$$

has only integral coefficients.

The next lemma is a generalization of that of Gauss (Theorem 3.6).

LEMMA 8.12. *Let*

$$p(x) = \alpha_p x^p + \alpha_{p-1}x^{p-1} + \cdots + \alpha_0 ,$$

$$q(x) = \beta_r x^r + \beta_{r-1}x^{r-1} + \cdots + \beta_0$$

be polynomials with integral coefficients, $\alpha_p\beta_r \neq 0$. Let

$$r(x) = p(x)q(x) = \gamma_s x^s + \gamma_{s-1}x^{s-1} + \cdots + \gamma_0 .$$

If δ is an integer such that all γ_k/δ are integers, so are all $\alpha_i\beta_j/\delta$.

For suppose

$$p(x) = \alpha_p(x - \rho_1) \cdots (x - \rho_p),$$

$$q(x) = \beta_r(x - \sigma_1) \cdots (x - \sigma_r);$$

then

$$\frac{r(x)}{\delta} = \frac{\alpha_p\beta_r}{\delta} (x - \rho_1) \cdots (x - \rho_p)(x - \sigma_1) \cdots (x - \sigma_r)$$

has integral coefficients. By Lemma 8.11 every product

$$(8.1) \qquad \frac{\alpha_p\beta_r}{\delta} \rho_{n_1} \rho_{n_2} \cdots \rho_{n_i} \sigma_{m_1} \sigma_{m_2} \cdots \sigma_{m_k}$$

is an integer. But α_i/α_p and β_j/β_r are elementary symmetric functions in the ρ_i and σ_i respectively, so that

$$\frac{\alpha_i\beta_j}{\delta} = \frac{\gamma_s}{\delta}\frac{\alpha_i}{\alpha_p}\frac{\beta_j}{\beta_r}$$

is a sum of terms of the form (8.1). Hence $\dfrac{\alpha_i\beta_j}{\delta}$ is an algebraic integer.

THEOREM 8.13. *For every ideal $A \neq (0)$ there is an ideal $B \neq (0)$ such that AB is principal. In fact we can find B so that $AB = (a)$, where a is a rational integer.*

Let $A = (\alpha_1, \cdots, \alpha_r)$ and define

$$g_i(x) = \alpha_1^{(i)}x + \alpha_2^{(i)}x^2 + \cdots + \alpha_r^{(i)}x^r, \; i = 1, \cdots, n,$$

where $\alpha_j^{(i)}$, $i = 1, \cdots, n$, are the conjugates of α_j for K. By an argument now familiar, the product

$$F(x) = g_1(x) \cdots g_n(x) = \sum c_p x^p$$

is a polynomial with rational integral coefficients. Moreover $g_1(x) \mid F(x)$, where we take $g_1(x)$ as the polynomial having the original α_i as coefficients. The quotient

$$h(x) = \frac{F(x)}{g_1(x)} = g_2(x) \cdots g_n(x)$$
$$= \beta_1 x + \cdots + \beta_m x^m$$

has coefficients which are integers in K.

Let a be the greatest common divisor of the c_p so that $F(x)/a$ is primitive. Define $B = (\beta_1, \cdots, \beta_m)$. We shall show that $AB = (a)$.

By Lemma 8.12 a divides all $\alpha_i\beta_j$. But AB is generated by all the products $\alpha_i\beta_j$. Hence $(a) \supset AB$. On the other hand, since a is the greatest common factor of the c_p, the rational integers c_k/a are relatively prime. Then there exist integers x_k such that*

$$1 = \sum x_k \frac{c_k}{a}, \qquad a = \sum x_k c_k .$$

But each c_k is, by its definition, of the form $\sum \lambda_{ijk}\alpha_i\beta_j$, so a is of the form $\sum_{i,j} \left(\sum_k x_k\lambda_{ijk}\right)\alpha_i\beta_j$. Then a is in AB, $AB \supset (a)$. So finally $(a) = AB$.

COROLLARY 8.14. *If $AB = AC$, $A \neq (0)$, then $B = C$*

For let $AD = (\delta)$, a principal ideal. Then $ABD = ACD$, $(\delta) B = (\delta) C$. Then δ times each integer in B equals δ times some integer in C, so each integer of B is in C, $C \supset B$. Similarly $B \supset C$, so that $B = C$.

COROLLARY 8.15. (*Converse of Lemma 8.3*). *If $A \supset B$, then $A \mid B$. In other words, a divisor is a factor.*

Choose D so that $AD = (\delta)$. Since $A \supset B$, $AD \supset BD$; this follows from the definition of multiplication of ideals. Write $BD = (\rho_1, \cdots, \rho_m)$. Each ρ_i is contained in $AD = (\delta)$, and is therefore of the form $\lambda_i\delta$. Hence

$$BD = (\delta) (\lambda_1, \lambda_2, \cdots, \lambda_m) = AD(\lambda_1, \lambda_2, \cdots, \lambda_m).$$

By Corollary 8.14, $B = A(\lambda_1, \lambda_2, \cdots, \lambda_m)$, so $A \mid B$.

COROLLARY 8.16. *An ideal is maximal if and only if it is irreducible.*

For it has now been established that factors and divisors are the same, so that an ideal which lacks one lacks the other.

LEMMA 8.17. *If $B \mid A$ and $B \neq A$, then B has fewer factors than A.*

This has already been proved in the course of establishing Lemma 8.9, since divisors and factors are now known to be the same thing.

---

* This can be proved in the same manner as Theorem 1.2.

LEMMA 8.18. *Every ideal not* (0) *or* (1) *can be factored into the product of irreducible ideals.*

By Lemma 8.9 the ideal A has a maximal divisor P_1, which by virtue of Corollary 8.15 is also a factor. Then $A = P_1 A_1$. If A_1 is (1) or maximal, stop here. Otherwise repeat the procedure with $A_1 = P_2 A_2$ to obtain $A = P_1 P_2 A_2$, and continue in this way. Eventually the procedure must stop, since each of A_1, A_2, $\cdots$ divides its predecessor, and so by Lemma 8.17 has fewer factors than the predecessor. We can conclude that $A = P_1 P_2 \cdots P_r$, where each P_i is maximal. By Corollary 8.16 each P_i is irreducible, and the lemma is proved.

To prove the uniqueness of the factorization we shall use the following consequence of Corollaries 8.8, 8.15, and 8.16.

LEMMA 8.19. *If P is an irreducible ideal and $P \mid AB$, then $P \mid A$ or $P \mid B$.*

THEOREM 8.20 (*The Fundamental Theorem*). *Every ideal not* (0) *or* (1) *can be factored into the product of irreducible ideals. This factorization is unique except for the order of the factors.*

The first part of the theorem has already been established as Lemma 8.18. We turn to the uniqueness. Suppose that the ideal A has two factorizations into irreducible ideals:

$$(8.2) \qquad A = P_1 P_2 \cdots P_r = P_1' P_2' \cdots P_s', \qquad s \geq r.$$

By Lemma 8.19 the ideal P_1' must divide one of the P_i, say P_1. Then $P_1' \mid P_1$, $P_1' \supset P_1$. But P_1 is maximal, and $P_1' \neq (1)$, so that $P_1' = P_1$. By Corollary 8.14 we can divide out P_1 in (8.2) to obtain

$$P_2 \cdots P_r = P_2' \cdots P_s'.$$

We can repeat this procedure until all the factors on the left-hand side are exhausted. Suppose there remains a factor P_i' on the right-hand side. Then $P_i' \mid (1)$, $P_i' \supset (1)$, $P_i' = (1)$. Hence all the factors on the right-hand side are also used up, so that, after some rearrangement of the order of the P_i if necessary, $P_i = P_i'$, $i = 1, \cdots r$, and $r = s$. The proof is complete.

3. **The modern proof.** The following version follows the outline given by Ore in his survey (see the bibliography). *We shall not make any use of the results obtained in §2.* Instead we shall proceed directly to a proof of a modified form of Theorem 8.20 in which "irreducible" is replaced by "maximal". As a *consequence* of this we shall then establish Corollaries 8.15 and 8.16. This will enable us to restore the word "irreducible" for "maximal", and thus prove Theorem 8.20 in its final form. The reader is reminded that the last theorem we are at liberty to use in this paragraph is Theorem 8.7 which asserts the equivalence of maximal and prime ideals. The equivalence of factors and divisors is established in §2, and this fact we cannot use without first offering a proof.

LEMMA 8.21. *An ideal A not (0) or (1) is a divisor of a product $P_1 \cdots P_s$ where each P_i is a divisor of A, and is a maximal ideal.*

If A is maximal there is nothing to prove. If it is not maximal, then by Theorem 8.7 A contains a product $\beta\gamma$ such that neither β nor γ belong to it. If $A = (\alpha_1, \cdots, \alpha_r)$, let

$$B = (\alpha_1, \cdots, \alpha_r, \beta), \qquad C = (\alpha_1, \cdots, \alpha_r, \gamma).$$

Then $A \supset BC$, $B \supset A$, $C \supset A$. Now repeat the procedure with B and C, and continue. At each stage the new ideals all include A and their product is included in A. But the procedure must stop, by Theorem 8.5, so that we finally reach maximal ideals.

Let P be a maximal ideal. We define P^{-1} as the totality of numbers α in the field K, *integers or not*, such that the product $\alpha\pi$ is an integer (not necessarily in P) for all numbers π in P.

LEMMA 8.22. *If P is a maximal ideal, P^{-1} contains a number which is not an algebraic integer.*

Let π, different from zero, be an integer in P and consider the principal ideal (π). (π) includes a product $P_1 \cdots P_r$ of maximal ideals, by the preceding lemma. If there are several such products, pick one for which r is least. Now $P \supset (\pi) \supset P_1 \cdots P_r$, so, by Corollary 8.8, P contains one of the P_i, say P_1. Since P_1 is maximal, $P = P_1$. The ideal (π) does not include $P_2 \cdots P_r$ since the product with the least number of factors was picked to begin with. Then $P_2 \cdots P_r$ contains an integer γ not in (π). Consequently γ/π is not an integer but $(\pi) \supset P P_2 \cdots P_r \supset P(\gamma)$. This means that if π' is in P then $\pi'\gamma$ is in (π). Then $\pi' \gamma/\pi$ is an integer. Hence γ/π is in P^{-1}.

If A is an ideal we define the product $AP^{-1} = P^{-1}A$ to be the set of all products $\alpha\beta$, where α is in A and β in P^{-1}.

LEMMA 8.23. *If P is a maximal ideal, then $PP^{-1} = (1)$.*

Let $A = PP^{-1}$. A is an ideal (why?). Since P^{-1} contains 1, $A \supset P$. But P is maximal, so that $A = (1)$ or $A = P$.

We assume that $A = P$. This will lead to a contradiction.

Let $\omega_1, \cdots, \omega_n$ be a basis for P, and let $\gamma_1 = \gamma/\pi$ be a non-integer in P^{-1} (see the preceding lemma). The products $\gamma_1\omega_i$ are all in $A = P$ and so can be represented as

$$\gamma_1 \omega_i = \sum_{j=1}^{n} a_{ij} \omega_j,$$

where the a_{ij} are rational integers. Then the system of equations

$$(a_{11} - \gamma_1)x_1 + a_{12}x_2 + \cdots = 0$$

$$a_{21}x_1 + (a_{22} - \gamma_1)x_2 + \cdots = 0$$

$$a_{n1}x_1 + \cdots + (a_{nn} - \gamma_1)x_n = 0$$

has a non-trivial solution $x_i = \omega_i$, so the determinant

$$\begin{vmatrix} a_{11} - \gamma_1 & a_{12} & \cdots & \cdots \\ a_{21} & a_{22} - \gamma_1 & \cdots & \cdots \\ \hdotsfor{4} \\ a_{n1} & a_{n2} & \cdots & a_{nn} - \gamma_1 \end{vmatrix}$$

vanishes. Hence γ_1 satisfies a monic equation with integral coefficients and is therefore an algebraic integer. This contradiction leads to the conclusion $A = (1)$.

LEMMA 8.24. *Every ideal A not (0) or (1) is the product of maximal ideals.*

By Lemma 8.21 A includes a product $P_1 \cdots P_r$ of maximal ideals, and as before we choose the product for which r is least. We proceed by induction on r.

If A includes only one maximal P, then $A = P$ and we are done. Suppose the theorem established for ideals which include a product of fewer than r factors. Since $A \supset P_1 \cdots P_r$, then $AP_r^{-1} \supset P_1 \cdots P_{r-1}$, by Lemma 8.23. By the hypothesis of the induction AP_r^{-1} is a product $P_1'P_2' \cdots P_k'$ of maximal ideals. By Lemma 8.23 once more $A = P_1'P_2' \cdots P_k'P_r$, so that A is a product of maximal ideals.

LEMMA 8.25. *Let $A = P_1 \cdots P_r$ and $B = Q_1 \cdots Q_s$ be products of maximal ideals each $\neq (1)$. If $B \supset A$, then each ideal Q occurs among the P at least as many times as it occurs in B.*

Since Q_1 is a factor of B it is a divisor of B (Lemma 8.3). Hence $Q_1 \supset B \supset A = P_1 \cdots P_r$. By Corollary 8.8, Q_1 contains one of the P_i, say P_1; so $Q_1 = P_1$, each being maximal and $\neq (1)$. Also

$$P_1^{-1}B \supset P_1^{-1}A = P_2 \cdots P_r,$$

by Lemma 8.23. The result then follows by induction if we assume it to be true when B contains fewer than r factors.

LEMMA 8.26. *The representation of an ideal as the product of maximal ideals is unique to within order.*

For suppose

$$A = P_1P_2 \cdots P_r = Q_1Q_2 \cdots Q_s.$$

Then we need only apply the preceding lemma with $A = B$. As a result of Lemma 8.24 and 8.26 we have

THEOREM 8.27. *An ideal different from* (0) *and* (1) *can be represented, uniquely apart from order, as the product of maximal ideals.*

In order to prove the fundamental Theorem 8.20 it is enough to show that the word "maximal" in the preceding theorem can be replaced by "irreducible". This is justifiable if we can prove that a divisor is a factor—in other words: if $B \supset A$, then $B \mid A$. But this in turn follows from Lemma 8.25. For we may write $A = P_1^{e_1} \cdots P_r^{e_r}$ and $B = P_1^{f_1} \cdots P_r^{f_r}$, where the P_i are the distinct maximal factors of A and B, and $e_i \geq f_i$. So $A = BC$, where $C = P_1^{e_1-f_1} \cdots P_r^{e_r-f_r}$. Hence the fundamental theorem is established.

From Theorem 8.7 and Corollary 8.16 it follows that irreducible, maximal and prime ideals are the same. The literature on algebraic numbers uses the last of these terms most frequently, and in the sequel we shall adhere to that tradition.

CHAPTER IX

CONSEQUENCES OF THE FUNDAMENTAL
THEOREM

1. **The highest common factor of two ideals.** Let A and
B be two ideals in the algebraic number field K. An ideal C
is said to be a *highest common factor of A and B*, written
(A, B), if $C \mid A$ and $C \mid B$, and if every ideal which divides
both A and B divides C. A highest common factor is
unique, for suppose both C and D have the requisite
properties. Then $C \mid D$ and $D \mid C$. By Lemma 8.3, $C \supset D$
and $D \supset C$, so that $C = D$.

There is a simple way of obtaining (A, B), as follows.
Let $A = (\alpha_1, \cdots, \alpha_r)$, $B = (\beta_1, \cdots, \beta_s)$. Define $D =
(\alpha_1, \cdots, \alpha_r, \beta_1, \cdots, \beta_s)$. Then $D = (A, B)$. For clearly
$D \supset A$, $D \supset B$ so that (Corollary 8.15) $D \mid A$, $D \mid B$.
Further suppose $E \mid A$, $E \mid B$. Then $E \supset A$, $E \supset B$,
so that $E \supset D$, hence $E \mid D$. Still another method of
obtaining the highest common factor of A and B is this:
Let $P_1, \cdots, P_r$ be the totality of distinct prime ideals
which occur in the factorizations of both A and B. Then
$(A, B) = P_1^{e_1} \cdots P_r^{e_r}$, where e_i is the highest power
(possibly zero*) for which $P_i^{e_i}$ divides both A and B.

THEOREM 9.1. *Two ideals A and B have a unique highest
common factor (A, B).*

If $(A, B) = (1)$ we say that A and B are *relatively prime*.
It is customary in this case to write simply $(A, B) = 1$.

We saw earlier (Theorem 7.11) that not every ideal in a
field K need be principal. We are now in a position to
show that in any case an ideal can always be generated
by *two* elements of K.

* It is convenient to define the power C^0 of an ideal C as (1).

LEMMA 9.2. *If A and B are ideals different from (0), there is an integer α in A such that*

$$\left(\frac{(\alpha)}{A}, B\right) = 1.$$

(If α is in A, then $A \supset (\alpha)$, $A \mid (\alpha)$, so it makes sense to speak of the ideal $(\alpha)/A$.)

If $B = (1)$ then the lemma is trivial, for there we can take for α any element of A. So we suppose that $B \neq (1)$.

Let $P_1, \cdots, P_r$ be the distinct prime factors of B. If $r = 1$ then $B = P^j$, $j > 0$, so we need only find an α in A for which

$$\left(\frac{(\alpha)}{A}, P\right) = 1.$$

Choose an integer α in A which is not in AP. One must exist, for otherwise $AP \supset A$, $AP \mid A$. Then since $A \neq (0)$, $P \mid (1)$, $P \supset (1)$, and $P = (1)$. This choice of α has the desired property. For $A \supset (\alpha)$, $A \mid (\alpha)$, so $(\alpha) = AC$ for some ideal C. Then $(C, P) = 1$, for if $(C, P) \neq 1$, C and P have the highest common factor P. Hence $C = PD$, $(\alpha) = APD$, $AP \mid (\alpha)$, $AP \supset (\alpha)$, contrary to the choice of α.

If $r > 1$, it is enough to find α so that

$$(9.1) \qquad \left(\frac{(\alpha)}{A}, P_m\right) = 1, \qquad m = 1, \cdots, r.$$

Consider the ideals $A_m = \dfrac{AP_1 \cdots P_r}{P_m}$ and P_m. By the preceding paragraph an element α_m of A_m can be chosen so that

$$(9.2) \qquad \left(\frac{(\alpha_m)}{A_m}, P_m\right) = 1.$$

Now let $\alpha = \alpha_1 + \cdots + \alpha_r$. Since $A \mid A_m$, $A \supset A_m$, and each α_m is in A. Therefore α is also in A.

If we can show that α is not in AP_m, then (9.1) is established. For if $(\alpha)/(A)$ and P_m have a common factor it must be P_m itself. In that event $(\alpha)/A = P_mD$, $(\alpha) = AP_mD$, so $AP_m \supset (\alpha)$—a contradiction.

To show that $\alpha = \alpha_1 + \cdots + \alpha_r$ is not in AP_m observe that each α_i, $i \neq m$, is in AP_m, for

$$(\alpha_i) \subset A_i = \frac{AP_1 \cdots P_r}{P_i} = AP_m \frac{P_1 \cdots P_r}{P_iP_m} \subset AP_m,$$

but α_m itself is not in AP_m, by (9.2).

THEOREM 9.3. *Let A be an ideal not zero, and β any non-zero element in it. Then we can find an α in A such that $A = (\alpha, \beta)$.*

Define $B = (\beta)/A$. By the preceding lemma there is an α in A such that

$$\left(\frac{(\alpha)}{A}, B\right) = \left(\frac{(\alpha)}{A}, \frac{(\beta)}{A}\right) = 1.$$

Let $(\alpha) = AC$, $C = (\alpha)/A$. Since $(\beta) = AB$ and $(B, C) = 1$, the highest common factor of (α) and (β) is A. By the remarks preceding Theorem 9.1 $A = (\alpha, \beta)$.

Observe that we have made frequent use of the quotient $(\alpha)/A$ when α is in A. In the future we shall write this as α/A and understand $A \mid \alpha$ to mean $A \mid (\alpha)$. α is in A if and only if $A \mid \alpha$. Another notation is $\alpha \equiv 0 \pmod{A}$ or $\alpha \equiv 0(A)$.

2. Unique factorization of integers.

We return now to the problem of unique factorization of integers in K, a question temporarily abandoned in Chapter VII. Our next theorem confirms a conjecture made there.

THEOREM 9.4. *The factorization of integers of K into primes is unique (to within order and units) if and only if all the ideals in K are principal.*

That such a factorization is possible has already been settled by Theorem 7.5.

First assume that all the ideals in K are principal. Suppose an element of K, not zero or a unit, has two factorizations into prime integers:

$$\alpha = \pi_1 \cdots \pi_s = \pi_1' \cdots \pi_t'.$$

Clearly

$$(9.3) \qquad (\alpha) = (\pi_1) \cdots (\pi_s) = (\pi_1') \cdots (\pi_t').$$

If π is a prime integer, then (π) is a prime ideal. For suppose $(\pi) = BC$. Since B and C are both principal by hypothesis, $(\pi) = (\beta)(\gamma) = (\beta\gamma)$. By Corollary 8.2, π and $\beta\gamma$ are associated, so one of β or γ is a unit. Hence one of B and C is the ideal (1), and (π) is prime. Then (9.3) gives two factorizations of (α) into prime ideals. By the uniqueness of factorization of ideals we must have $s = t$, and $(\pi_i) = (\pi_i')$ after a suitable rearrangement of factors. Moreover, π_i/π_i' is a unit. This proves the sufficiency.

Suppose, conversely, that factorization of integers is unique. To prove that every ideal is principal it is enough to prove that every prime ideal P is principal. According to Theorem 8.13, $P \mid a$ for some rational integer a. Let $a = \pi_1 \cdots \pi_r$ be the factorization of a into prime integers in K. Then $(a) = (\pi_1) \cdots (\pi_r)$, so that $P \mid \pi$ for some prime integer π in K. (We do not claim that (π) is a prime ideal.) So $(\pi) = PA$. Then π is in both P and A, for also $A \mid \pi$. By Theorem 9.3 we can write $P = (\pi, \gamma)$, $A = (\pi, \delta)$, so that

$$(\pi) = (\pi, \gamma) (\pi, \delta) = (\pi, \gamma\delta).$$

It follows that $\pi \mid \gamma\delta$. From the unique factorization $\pi \mid \gamma$ or $\pi \mid \delta$.

We shall exclude the second possibility. If $\pi \mid \delta$, then $A = (\pi, \delta) = (\pi)$, $(\pi) = PA = P(\pi)$, so $P = (1)$. This is impossible since P is prime. The only alternative is $\pi \mid \gamma$. But then $P = (\pi, \gamma) = (\pi)$, and P is principal, as desired.

We shall now present a criterion for the principality of all ideals in K—that is, for uniqueness of factorization of integers. It is due to Dedekind and Hasse.

THEOREM 9.5. *Every ideal in K is principal if, and only if, for every two integers α and β, neither zero, such that $\beta \nmid \alpha$ and $\mid N\alpha \mid \geq \mid N\beta \mid$, there exist integers γ and δ such that*

$$0 < \mid N(\alpha\gamma - \beta\delta) \mid < \mid N\beta \mid.$$

First suppose that every ideal in K is principal. Let α, β be integers of the prescribed kind and let $A = (\alpha, \beta)$. Since A is principal $(\alpha, \beta) = (\omega)$, so every integer in A is a multiple of ω. In particular $\beta = \sigma\omega$, $N\beta = N\sigma N\omega$. β and ω are not associated, for otherwise $\beta \mid \alpha$ since we know that $\omega \mid \alpha$. Hence $\mid N\sigma \mid > 1$, so that $\mid N\omega \mid < \mid N\beta \mid$. But ω is in (α, β), so $\omega = \alpha\gamma - \beta\delta$, and therefore $\mid N(\alpha\gamma - \beta\delta) \mid < \mid N\beta \mid$. Finally $\omega \neq 0$, since $\beta = \sigma\omega$, so that $\mid N(\omega) \mid > 0$.

Conversely, suppose the criterion to be satisfied and let A be any non-zero ideal in K. By Theorem 9.3 we can write it as $A = (\alpha, \beta)$. Let ω be a non-zero element of A for which $\mid N(\omega) \mid$ is least. Then $A = (\omega)$, for if γ is any integer in A such that $\omega \nmid \gamma$ we can find a combination $\mu\gamma - \nu\omega$ in A such that

$$0 < \mid N(\mu\gamma - \nu\omega) \mid < \mid N\omega \mid.$$

This contradicts the choice of ω, so there can be no γ in A for which $\omega \nmid \gamma$.

The criterion just established is unfortunately very

difficult to apply in practice. Sometimes it is possible
to apply it with $\gamma = 1$. In this case the field is called
Euclidean. The number of real Euclidean quadratic fields
is finite. (See Hardy and Wright, Chapter XIV, for a
discussion of this and the following remarks.) The only
imaginary quadratic fields $R(\sqrt{D})$, D square-free, whch
are Euclidean are those for which $D = -1, -2, -3, -7,$
-11. In addition, the following satisfy the more general
Dedekind-Hasse criterion: $D = -19, -43, -67, -163.$
It is known that there can be at most one more imaginary
quadratic field in which all ideals are principal, and that
if it exists the corresponding D is numerically larger than
five billion!

In summary, the problem of unique factorization of
integers is now reduced to another, but the new one is
far from completely solved. Nevertheless, as we shall see
in the sequel, the theory of ideals has far more important
consequences than Theorems 9.4 and 9.5.

3. **The problem of ramification.** As we shall see later
in this chapter, each prime ideal P in an algebraic number
field K divides exactly one ideal (p), where p is a rational
prime. This means that the prime ideals in K can be
detected by considering the complete factorization
$(p) = P_1 \cdots P_r$ of each ideal (p) into prime ideals P_i
of K. An important question which occurs is this: when
does (p) have a repeated factor P_i and when are all the P_i
distinct? In the former case (p) is said to be *ramified*;
otherwise *unramified*. The answer is given by the following
theorem of Dedekind. (p) is unramified if and only if
$p \nmid d$, where d is the discriminant of K. A complete proof is
difficult,* and we shall prove only this part of the theorem:
if $p \nmid d$ then (p) is not divisible by the square of a prime
ideal.

* See, for example, Landau's *Vorlesungen* III.

Let α be an integer in K, and $\alpha_1, \cdots, \alpha_n$ its conjugates for K. We define $S(\alpha)$, the *trace* of α, by

$$S(\alpha) = \alpha_1 + \cdots + \alpha_n .$$

Since $-S(\alpha)$ is the second coefficient of the field polynomial for α, $S(\alpha)$ is a rational integer. Moreover $S(a\alpha) = aS(\alpha)$, for any rational number a.

Now suppose that (p) has a square factor P^2. We shall prove that $p \mid d$. Let $(p) = P^2Q$. Choose α so that $PQ \mid \alpha$, $P^2Q \nmid \alpha$. Then $\alpha \neq 0$ and $p \nmid \alpha$. Moreover, since $P^2Q \mid P^2Q^2$, $P^2Q^2 \mid (\alpha)^2$, and $(\alpha)^2 = (\alpha^2)$, it follows that $p \mid \alpha^2$. Since $p \geq 2$, $\alpha^2 \mid \alpha^p\beta^p$ for any integer β in K. Hence $p \mid \alpha^p\beta^p$, and $\dfrac{(\alpha\beta)^p}{p}$ is an integer in K. By the remarks of the preceding paragraph

$$S\left(\frac{(\alpha\beta)^p}{p}\right) = \frac{S((\alpha\beta)^p)}{p}$$

is a rational integer, so that $S((\alpha\beta)^p)$ belongs to (p). Let $\beta_1, \cdots, \beta_n$ be the conjugates of β. Then

$$\begin{aligned}
(S(\alpha\beta))^p &= (\alpha_1\beta_1 + \alpha_2\beta_2 + \cdots + \alpha_n\beta_n)^p \\
&= (\alpha_1\beta_1)^p + (\alpha_2\beta_2)^p + \cdots + (\alpha_n\beta_n)^p + p\gamma \\
&= S((\alpha\beta)^p) + p\gamma
\end{aligned}$$

where γ is an integer in K. Hence $(S(\alpha\beta))^p$ also belongs to (p), for any integer β in K. Since $(S(\alpha\beta))^p$ is a rational integer, $p \mid S(\alpha\beta)$.

Now let $\omega_1, \cdots, \omega_n$ be an integral basis for K. Then $\alpha = \sum_{k=1}^{n} h_k\omega_k$, where the h_k are rational integers. Since $p \nmid \alpha$ not all the h_k are divisible by p. But

$$S(\alpha\omega_i) = S(\sum_k h_k\omega_k\omega_i) = \sum_k h_k S(\omega_k\omega_i).$$

Since $p \mid S(\alpha\omega_i)$, we can conclude that p divides the last sum. For simplicity let $a_{ki} = S(\omega_k\omega_i)$, and $\Delta = \mid a_{ki} \mid$. We shall show that $p \mid \Delta$.

Let A_{ki} be the cofactor of a_{ki} in the determinant Δ. Then

$$\sum_i A_{ij} \sum_k a_{ki} h_k = \sum_k h_k \sum_i A_{ij} a_{ki} = \Delta h_j.$$

Since p divides each sum $\sum_k a_{ki}h_k$, p divides Δh_j for each j. But not all the h_j are divisible by p. Hence $p \mid \Delta$.

It remains only to identify Δ with $d = [\omega_1, \cdots, \omega_n]$. Denote by $\omega_i^{(j)}$ the conjugates of ω_i. By the multiplication of determinants

$$d = \mid \omega_j^{(i)} \mid^2 = \begin{vmatrix} \omega_1^{(1)} & \cdots & \omega_1^{(n)} \\ & \cdots & \\ \omega_n^{(1)} & \cdots & \omega_n^{(n)} \end{vmatrix} \cdot \begin{vmatrix} \omega_1^{(1)} & \cdots & \omega_n^{(1)} \\ & \cdots & \\ \omega_1^{(n)} & \cdots & \omega_n^{(n)} \end{vmatrix}$$

$$= \mid \sum_j \omega_k^{(j)} \omega_i^{(j)} \mid = \mid S(\omega_k \omega_i) \mid = \Delta.$$

We have established the desired result.

THEOREM 9.6. *If $p \nmid d$, then (p) is unramified.*

COROLLARY 9.7. *Let $K = R(\zeta)$, where ζ is a primitive p^{th} root of unity, p a rational prime. If q is a rational prime different from p, then (q) is unramified in K.*

This is a consequence of the fact that $q \nmid d$, since $d = (-1)^{(p-1)/2} p^{p-2}$ (Theorem 6.13).

4. **Congruences and norms.** Our next aim is to clear the way for a proof of the assertion made in Chapter VII, that an ideal is the totality of integers in K divisible by a fixed integer (not necessarily in K). The reader will find it useful at this stage to review the notion of congruence discussed in §2 of Chapter II.

Let A be an ideal. We define α and β to be *congruent modulo A* (written $\alpha \equiv \beta \pmod{A}$ or $\alpha \equiv \beta(A)$) if $\alpha - \beta$ is in A or, what is the same, if $A \mid (\alpha - \beta)$. The rules for operating with such congruence statements are those stated in the earlier chapter.

If α is a fixed integer in K, we call the set of all integers congruent to α modulo A a *residue class* modulo A. α is called a *representative* of the class. For example, by Theorem 7.11, every ideal in R must take the form (m), and $0, 1, \cdots, m - 1$ are representatives of the m residue classes modulo (m).

THEOREM 9.8. *If $A \neq (0)$ is an ideal in K, the number of residue classes modulo A is finite.*

According to Theorem 8.13 we can choose an ideal B so that $AB = (a)$, where a is a rational integer. If $\mu \equiv \nu(a)$, then $\mu \equiv \nu(A)$, for $A \supset a$ since $A \mid a$. But the number of residue classes in K modulo (a) is finite, as the proof of Lemma 8.4 shows. Since $\mu \not\equiv \nu(A)$ implies $\mu \not\equiv \nu(\bmod (a))$, it follows that the number of residue classes modulo A is finite.

The number of residue classes modulo A is called the *norm* of A, written NA or $N(A)$. If A is principal, say $A = (\alpha)$, we write $N((\alpha))$ for the norm, since the notation $N(\alpha)$ can be taken for the norm of the integer α, and the two norms may not be the same in value. Observe that $NA = 1$ if and only if $A = (1)$.

The reader will recall that every non-zero ideal has a basis of integers (Theorem 7.10). We now prove a little more.

LEMMA 9.9. *If $\omega_1, \cdots, \omega_n$ is an integral basis for the algebraic number field K, then each ideal $A \neq (0)$ in it has a basis $\alpha_1, \cdots, \alpha_n$ of the form*

$$\begin{aligned}
\alpha_1 &= a_{11}\omega_1, \\
\alpha_2 &= a_{21}\omega_1 + a_{22}\omega_2, \\
&\cdots\cdots\cdots\cdots\cdots\cdots \\
\alpha_n &= a_{n1}\omega_1 + \cdots + a_{nn}\omega_n,
\end{aligned}$$

where the a_{ij} are rational integers and all the a_{ii} are positive.

Let $AB = (a)$, where a is a rational integer not zero. Since a is in A, so are $a\omega_1, \cdots, a\omega_n$. Let m be fixed, $1 \leq m \leq n$. From all the elements of A which are of the form $a_1\omega_1 + \cdots + a_m\omega_m$, where the a_i are rational integers and $a_m > 0$ (there is at least one such element, since $a\omega_m$ and $-a\omega_m$ are in A), choose that element

$$\alpha_m = a_{m1}\omega_1 + \cdots + a_{mm}\omega_m$$

for which $a_m = a_{mm}$ is least. The α_i, $i = 1, \cdots, n$, so defined have the properties stated in the lemma.

First, the α_i form a basis for K, by Theorem 5.4, since the determinant

$$\begin{vmatrix} a_{11} & 0 & \cdots & 0 \\ a_{21} & a_{22} & 0 & \cdots \\ \hdotsfor{4} \\ a_{n1} & a_{n2} & \cdots & a_{nn} \end{vmatrix} = a_{11}\, a_{22} \cdots a_{nn}$$

is different from zero. We shall show that the α_i also form a basis for A.

Let α be an integer in A. Since the ω_i form an integral basis for K, we can write

$$\alpha = b_1\omega_1 + \cdots + b_n\omega_n,$$

where the b_i are rational integers. By Theorem 1.1

$$b_n = h_n a_{nn} + r_n, \qquad 0 \leq r_n < a_{nn}$$

and therefore

$$\alpha - h_n\alpha_n = \alpha - h_n(a_{n1}\omega_1 + \cdots + a_{nn}\omega_n)$$
$$= b_1'\omega_1 + \cdots + b_{n-1}'\omega_{n-1} + r_n\omega_n$$

is in A. By the definition of a_{nn} we must have $r_n = 0$; then

$$\alpha - h_n\alpha_n = b_1'\omega_1 + \cdots + b_{n-1}'\omega_{n-1}.$$

Now repeat the procedure with b_{n-1}' to obtain

$$\alpha - h_n\alpha_n - h_{n-1}\alpha_{n-1} = b_1''\omega_1 + \cdots + b_{n-2}''\omega_{n-2},$$

and continue until

$$\alpha - h_n\alpha_n - \cdots - h_1\alpha_1 = 0,$$
$$\alpha = h_1\alpha_1 + \cdots + h_n\alpha_n.$$

Hence α can be expressed in terms of the α_i with rational integral coefficients. The representation is unique since the α_i are a basis for K.

This lemma enables us to obtain an explicit formula for the norm of an ideal.

THEOREM 9.10. *If A is an ideal in K and $\alpha_1, \cdots, \alpha_n$ is a basis for A, then*

$$NA = \left| \frac{\Delta[\alpha_1, \cdots, \alpha_n]}{d} \right|^{1/2},$$

where d is the discriminant of K.

First note that every basis for A has the same discriminant. This follows from the argument used to prove Theorem 6.10. So we can take for the basis of A the one described in Lemma 9.9. By formula (5.1)

$$\Delta[\alpha_1, \cdots, \alpha_n] = \begin{vmatrix} a_{11} & 0 & \cdots & 0 \\ a_{21} & a_{22} & 0 & \cdots \\ \cdots\cdots\cdots\cdots\cdots\cdots \\ a_{n1} & a_{n2} & \cdots & a_{nn} \end{vmatrix}^2 \Delta[\omega_1, \cdots, \omega_n].$$

By Theorem 6.10 $d = \Delta[\omega_1, \cdots, \omega_n]$, so that

$$\Delta[\alpha_1, \cdots, \alpha_n] = (a_{11}a_{12} \cdots a_{nn})^2 d.$$

The formula of the theorem reduces to $NA = a_{11} \cdots a_{nn}$.

This means we need only show that $a_{11} \cdots a_{nn}$ is the number of distinct residue classes modulo A. For this it suffices to show that

(i) no pair of the $a_{11} \cdots a_{nn}$ numbers

$$r_1\omega_1 + \cdots + r_n\omega_n, \qquad 0 \le r_n < a_{nn},$$

is congruent modulo A;

(ii) every integer in K is congruent to one of these numbers modulo A.

To prove (i) suppose that

$$r_1\omega_1 + \cdots + r_n\omega_n \equiv r_1'\omega_1 + \cdots + r_n'\omega_n \ (A),$$

where $0 \leq r_n < a_{nn}$, $0 \leq r_n' < a_{nn}$. We may suppose that $r_n > r_n'$. Hence

$$(r_1 - r_1')\omega_1 + \cdots + (r_{n-1} - r_{n-1}')\omega_{n-1}$$
$$+ (r_n - r_n')\omega_n \equiv 0(A).$$

By the definition of a_{nn}, $r_n - r_n' = 0$, $r_n = r_n'$. A similar argument shows that $r_i = r_i'$, $i = 1, \cdots, n - 1$.

We prove (ii). Each integer α in the field has the form

$$\alpha = b_1\omega_1 + \cdots + b_n\omega_n$$

for rational integers b_i. Let

$$b_n = h_n a_{nn} + r_n, \qquad 0 \leq r_n < a_{nn}.$$

Then

$$\alpha - h_n\alpha_n = b_1'\omega_1 + \cdots + b_{n-1}'\omega_{n-1} + r_n\omega_n.$$

Repeating this procedure with b_{n-1}', b_{n-2}'', $\cdots$, we have

$$\alpha - h_n\alpha_n - \cdots - h_1\alpha_1 = r_1\omega_1 + \cdots + r_n\omega_n$$

where $0 \leq r_m < a_{mm}$, so that $\alpha \equiv r_1\omega_1 + \cdots + r_n\omega_n$ modulo A.

COROLLARY 9.11. *If A is principal, $A = (\alpha)$, then $NA = |N\alpha|$.*

Clearly $\alpha\omega_1, \cdots, \alpha\omega_n$ is a basis for A, and

$$\Delta[\alpha\omega_1, \cdots, \alpha\omega_n] = (N\alpha)^2\Delta[\omega_1, \cdots, \omega_n] = (N\alpha)^2 d.$$

But by the theorem $\Delta[\alpha\omega_1, \cdots, \alpha\omega_n] = (NA)^2 d$: Hence $(N\alpha)^2 = (NA)^2$. Since $NA > 0$, the corollary follows.

5. **Further properties of norms.** In reading this section the reader will find it instructive to examine each of our

results for the special case $K = R$ and to compare them with the analogous work done in Chapter II.

LEMMA 9.12. *The congruence*

$$\alpha\xi \equiv \beta\ (A), \qquad ((\alpha),\ A) = 1,$$

has a solution ξ which is unique modulo A.

Let $\xi_1,\ \cdots,\ \xi_{NA}$ be a *complete residue system* modulo A—that is, a set of representatives, one from each residue class. Since $\alpha \neq 0$, the set $\alpha\xi_1,\ \cdots,\ \alpha\xi_{NA}$ is also a complete residue system. For if $\alpha\xi_1 \equiv \alpha\xi_2$, then $A \mid \alpha(\xi_1 - \xi_2)$. Thus $A \mid (\xi_1 - \xi_2)$ since $((\alpha),\ A) = 1$, so that $\xi_1 \equiv \xi_2(A)$ and $\xi_1 = \xi_2$. Then among the $\alpha\xi_i$ there is exactly one which is congruent to β modulo A.

THEOREM 9.13. *The congruence*

$$\alpha\xi \equiv \beta(A)$$

has a solution ξ if and only if $\beta \equiv 0(D)$, where $D = ((\alpha),\ A)$. If there is a solution it is unique modulo A/D.

If ξ is a solution of the congruence, then $\alpha\xi - \beta = \rho$ is in A, $A \mid \rho$. But then $D \mid \rho$, $D \mid \alpha$; so $D \mid \beta$, and β is in D.

Conversely, suppose β is in D. By the definition of D we can find $\alpha\xi$ in (α) and κ in A so that $\alpha\xi + \kappa = \beta$. Then $\alpha\xi \equiv \beta(A)$.

If $\alpha\xi$, $\alpha\xi'$ are both congruent to β, then $\alpha(\xi - \xi') \equiv 0$, $A \mid \alpha(\xi - \xi')$. Let $A = DA_1$, $(\alpha) = DA_2$, where A_1 and A_2 are relatively prime. Then

$$DA_1 \mid DA_2(\xi - \xi'),\ A_1 \mid A_2(\xi - \xi'),\ A_1 \mid (\xi - \xi'),\ \xi \equiv \xi'(A_1),$$

and finally $\xi \equiv \xi'(A/D)$.

THEOREM 9.14. $N(AB) = NA \cdot NB$.

The theorem is trivial if either A or B is (0). Hence we assume A, $B \neq (0)$. Then, according to Lemma 9.2 it is possible to find γ in A such that $((\gamma)/A,\ B) = 1$, or $((\gamma),\ AB) = A$. Let $\alpha_1,\ \cdots,\ \alpha_{NA}$ and $\beta_1,\ \cdots,\ \beta_{NB}$ be complete residue systems modulo A and B respectively.

Then no two of the $NA \cdot NB$ numbers $\alpha_i + \gamma\beta_j$ can be congruent modulo AB. For if $\alpha + \gamma\beta \equiv \alpha' + \gamma\beta'(AB)$, then $\alpha + \gamma\beta \equiv \alpha' + \gamma\beta'(A)$. But γ is in A so that $\alpha \equiv \alpha'(A)$. Since α and α' are elements of a complete residue system, $\alpha = \alpha'$. Hence $\gamma(\beta - \beta') \equiv 0(AB)$. Since $((\gamma), AB) = A$, $(\gamma) = AC$ where $(C, B) = 1$. So $B \mid (\beta - \beta')$. Hence $\beta \equiv \beta'(B)$, $\beta = \beta'$.

To prove the theorem it remains only to show that each integer α in the field K is congruent to one of the numbers $\alpha_i + \gamma\beta_j$ modulo AB. Choose α_i so that $\alpha_i \equiv \alpha(A)$. Now consider the congruence $\gamma\xi \equiv \alpha - \alpha_i(AB)$. By Theorem 9.13 it has a solution since $\alpha - \alpha_i$ is in $A = ((\gamma), AB)$. Moreover ξ can be chosen uniquely modulo $\dfrac{AB}{A} = B$, so ξ is one of the β_j. Then $\alpha \equiv \alpha_i + \gamma\beta_j(AB)$.

COROLLARY 9.15. *If NA is prime, so is A.*

THEOREM 9.16. *NA is an element of A.*

Let $\alpha_1, \cdots, \alpha_{NA}$ be a complete residue system; $\alpha_1 + 1$, $\cdots, \alpha_{NA} + 1$ is one also, so that

$$\alpha_1 + \cdots + \alpha_{NA} \equiv (\alpha_1 + 1) + \cdots + (\alpha_{NA} + 1) \ (A),$$
$$0 \equiv NA \ (A).$$

COROLLARY 9.17. *There are only a finite number of ideals of given norm.*

For NA can belong to only a finite number of ideals (Lemma 8.4).

THEOREM 9.18 (*Fermat's theorem*). *If P is a prime ideal in K and $P \nmid \alpha$, then*

$$\alpha^{NP-1} \equiv 1(P).$$

Let $\alpha_1, \cdots, \alpha_{NP}$ be a complete residue system modulo P. Then $\alpha\alpha_1, \cdots, \alpha\alpha_{NP}$ is also such a system. One member of each list, say α_{NP} and $\alpha\alpha_{NP}$, is divisible by P. Omitting these and multiplying the other members of each list together, we find that

$$\alpha_1 \cdots \alpha_{NP-1} \equiv \alpha^{NP-1}\alpha_1 \cdots \alpha_{NP-1}(P).$$

Since $P \nmid \alpha_1 \cdots \alpha_{NP-1}$, $1 \equiv \alpha^{NP-1}(P)$.

We conclude with a proof of the theorem mentioned at the beginning of §3.

THEOREM 9.19. *If* P *is prime it divides exactly one positive rational prime* p. *Then* $NP = p^f$, *where* $1 \leq f \leq n$ *and* n *is the degree of* K *over* R.

By Theorem 8.13, $P \mid a$ for some rational integer a. If $a = p_1 \cdots p_n$ is the factorization of a into rational primes, then $(a) = (p_1) \cdots (p_n)$. Hence $P \mid (p_i)$ for some value of i. Let $p = |p_i|$. Then $P \mid p$.

If $P \mid p$, $P \mid q$ where p and q are distinct primes, then we can find rational integers m and n such that $mp + nq = 1$. So $P \mid 1$, $P \supset (1)$, contrary to the fact that P is prime.

Finally, by Corollary 9.11, $N((p)) = |Np| = p^n$. Since $P \mid p$, $NP \mid N((p))$, so $NP = p^f$, $1 \leq f \leq n$.

CHAPTER X

CLASS NUMBERS AND FERMAT'S PROBLEM

1. **Class numbers.** We are almost ready now to fulfill the promise made earlier of a proof that each ideal is the totality of integers in $K = R(\theta)$ which are divisible (in the extended sense) by some integer, not necessarily in K. Our proof will rest on the notion of class number.

In order not to interrupt the argument, we shall anticipate one theorem to be proved in the next chapter. The proof is based on a new idea whose introduction we prefer to postpone for the moment.

THEOREM 10.1. *If K is a field different from R and A an ideal in K different from zero, there is a number $\alpha \neq 0$ in A such that*

$$| N\alpha | < N(A)\sqrt{| d |}.$$

Two ideals A and B in K are *equivalent*, written $A \sim B$, if there are two non-zero integers α and β in K such that

$$(\alpha)A = (\beta)B.$$

The simplest properties of this equivalence relation are the following:

(i) $A \sim A$;

(ii) $A \sim B$ if and only if $B \sim A$;

(iii) if $A \sim B$ and $B \sim C$, then $A \sim C$;

(iv) all principal ideals are equivalent; all ideals equivalent to a principal ideal are principal.

The totality of ideals in K equivalent to a fixed ideal $A \neq (0)$ is said to constitute a *class*. The number of classes (which we shall soon show to be finite) is called the *class-number* h of K. If the class-number is 1 then all ideals are equivalent to (1) and so are all principal. From Theorem 9.4 it follows that a field has unique factorization of integers into prime integers if and only if its class-number is 1.

THEOREM 10.2. *The class-number h of a field is finite.*

If the field is R, $h = 1$, and there is nothing to prove. If K is not R it is enough to show that in each class of ideals there is an ideal B such that $NB < \sqrt{|d|}$, for then $(NB)^2 = 1, 2, \cdots$, or $|d| - 1$, and by Corollary 9.17 there are only a finite number of ideals of given norm.

Let a class be given, and let C be any ideal in it. Choose A so that AC is principal; then $AC \sim (1)$. By the preceding theorem we can find $\alpha \neq 0$ in A so that $|N\alpha| < N(A) \sqrt{|d|}$. Since $A \mid \alpha$, $(\alpha) = AB$ for some ideal B, $N((\alpha)) = |N\alpha| = NA \cdot NB$, so that $NA \cdot NB < N(A) \sqrt{|d|}$, $NB < \sqrt{|d|}$. It remains only to show that $B \sim C$. But $AB \sim (1)$, $AC \sim (1)$, so that $AB \sim AC$, and the result follows.

COROLLARY 10.3. *If A is an ideal in K, and h is the class-number of K, then A^h is principal.*

If $A = (0)$, $A^h = (0)$ and the result is clear. Suppose that $A \neq (0)$. Choose a set of ideals $A_1, \cdots, A_h$, one from each class in K. Then $AA_1, \cdots, AA_h$ fall into distinct classes, for if $AA_i \sim AA_j$ then $A_i \sim A_j$. Hence

$$A_1 \cdots A_h \sim AA_1 \cdot AA_2 \cdots AA_h = A^h A_1 \cdots A_h,$$

so $A^h \sim (1)$ and A^h is principal.

COROLLARY 10.4. *If p is a rational prime, $p \nmid h$, and $A^p \sim B^p$, then $A \sim B$.*

We have $(\alpha)A^p = (\beta)B^p$. Since p and h are relatively prime we can find positive rational integers r and s so that $pr - hs = 1$. Then

$$(\alpha)^r A^{pr} = (\beta)^r B^{pr},$$
$$(\alpha)^r A A^{hs} = (\beta)^r B B^{hs}.$$

But A^h and B^h are principal; hence so are $(\alpha)^r A^{hs}$ and $(\beta)^r B^{hs}$. It follows that $A \sim B$.

We shall now prove that any ideal in K is the totality of integers α in K which are divisible by a fixed integer κ, not necessarily in K. It must not be supposed that κ is unique, even to within units. For example, let $A = (2)$ in R, the rational field. Then A consists of all the even rational integers—that is, the totality of integers in R divisible by 2. But A is also the totality of integers in R divisible by $\sqrt{2}$ (in the extended sense of division). For $n/\sqrt{2}$ is an algebraic integer if n is even, but not if n is odd. But there is uniqueness in this sense: among all the κ which have the desired property there is one which is divisible by all the others; *this* one is unique to within units. In the special case just considered, the integer 2 is the one which contains all other κ as factors. Of course -2 serves equally well.

THEOREM 10.5. *For each ideal A in K there is an integer κ, not necessarily in K, such that*

(i) *A is the totality of integers δ in K for which δ/κ is integral;*

(ii) *every integer κ' with property* (i) *divides κ.*

κ is unique to within units.

Let $A = (\alpha, \beta)$. Then $(\alpha, \beta)^h = (\omega)$ is principal, by Corollary 10.3. $\kappa = \omega^{1/h}$ is an integer since it satisfies the equation $x^h - \omega = 0$. Consider the extension $E = K(\kappa)$ of K. E contains K and hence all the elements of A. Now in K

$$A^h = (\alpha, \beta)^h = (\omega).$$

By Theorem 8.1 these ideals are equal when considered as ideals in any finite extension of K. Then $(\alpha, \beta)^h = (\omega) = (\kappa)^h$ in E. In view of the unique factorization theorem for ideals in E, $(\alpha, \beta) = (\kappa)$, still in E. Hence every element of A is divisible by κ. Moreover

$$(10.1) \qquad\qquad \kappa = \lambda\alpha + \nu\beta,$$

where λ and ν are in E.

Conversely we must show that any element γ in K which is divisible by κ is in A. Since γ and κ are both in E, and $\kappa \mid \gamma$ it follows that γ is in $(\kappa) = (\alpha, \beta)$, *where* (α, β) *is considered as an ideal in* E. We wish to show that γ is in (α, β) when (α, β) is considered as an ideal in K—this is not yet clear. But $\gamma = \lambda\kappa$, where λ is an integer in E. Let κ be of degree k over K. Then $E = K(\kappa)$, $(E/K) = k$. Let $\kappa_1, \kappa_2, \cdots, \kappa_k$ denote the conjugates of κ and $\lambda_1, \cdots, \lambda_k$ the conjugates of λ for E. γ is in K so that all its conjugates are the same. Hence

$$\gamma = \lambda_i\kappa_i, \; i = 1, \cdots, k; \qquad \gamma^k = (\lambda_1 \cdots \lambda_k)(\kappa_1 \cdots \kappa_k).$$

The product $\xi = \lambda_1 \cdots \lambda_k$ is symmetric in the λ_i, so it is an integer in K. Since κ satisfies $x^h - \omega = 0$, so does each of $\kappa_1, \cdots, \kappa_k$. Then

$$\kappa_i^h = \omega, \qquad (\kappa_1 \cdots \kappa_k)^h = \omega^k, \qquad \gamma^{hk} = \xi^h\omega^k;$$

hence, as ideals in K,

$$(\gamma)^{hk} = (\xi)^h(\omega)^k = (\xi)^h A^{hk},$$
$$(\gamma)^k = (\xi)A^k, \qquad A^k \mid (\gamma)^k$$

by the fundamental theorem of ideal theory. By another application of this theorem it follows that $A \mid \gamma$, so that γ is in A. This proves part (i) of the theorem, and (ii) follows from (10.1).

To prove the uniqueness of κ suppose that κ_1 and κ_2 both have properties (i) and (ii). Then $\kappa_1 \mid \kappa_2$, $\kappa_2 \mid \kappa_1$ so that $\kappa_2 = \sigma\kappa_1$, where σ is a unit.

2. The Fermat Conjecture. The reader is probably familiar with the famous unsolved problem: for what positive integral values of n does the equation

$$(10.2) \qquad x^n + y^n = z^n$$

have a solution in rational integers? For $n = 2$ there are solutions—for example, $3^2 + 4^2 = 5^2$. It is an easy matter to prove that there can be no solution for $n = 4$; the proof depends only on the simplest properties of integers and can be found in almost any book on elementary number theory. It was asserted by Fermat in 1637 that if $n > 2$ there are never any solutions (Fermat's "Last" Theorem), but a proof has never been found and the assertion at present has only the status of a conjecture. A large part of the theory of algebraic numbers originated in an effort to prove it.

Before discussing the conjecture further we shall simplify its statement somewhat. Since there is no solution for $n = 4$ there can be no solution when $n = 4m$, for we can write the equation (10.2) as $(x^m)^4 + (y^m)^4 = (z^m)^4$. Every integer $n \neq 4m$, $n > 2$, can be written in the form $n = pr$, where p is an odd prime; hence it is enough to show that (10.2) has no solutions when n is an odd prime. For we can write $(x^r)^p + (y^r)^p = (z^r)^p$. Finally, we let $n = p$ and replace z by $-z$; since p is odd (10.2) becomes

$$(10.3) \qquad x^p + y^p + z^p = 0.$$

Fermat's conjecture then amounts to this: for no odd prime p does (10.3) have a solution in rational integers.

It is convenient to classify the primes p as follows. Let h be the class-number of $K(\zeta)$, where ζ is a primitive p^{th} root of unity. If $p \nmid h$, p is *regular*; otherwise p is *irregular*. Kummer proved that if p is regular, then (10.3) has no solution in rational integers. Unfortunately there are an infinite number of irregular primes and for them the status of (10.3) is unsettled to this day. We shall illustrate the connection of Fermat's conjecture with algebraic number theory by proving a weakened version of Kummer's theorem. The reader who wishes to know more about this subject should consult volume III of Landau's *Vorlesungen* or Vandiver's expository paper listed in the bibliography.

A series of lemmas will be proved first. ζ will have the same meaning as usual—a primitive p^{th} root of unity, $p \neq 2$. $K = R(\zeta)$ is of degree $p - 1$ over R. To avoid a real danger of confusion, ideals will be written in *square brackets* rather than parentheses. As earlier, λ will denote $1 - \zeta$. L denotes the ideal $[\lambda]$.

LEMMA 10.6. $L^{p-1} = [p]$ and $NL = p$.

As we proved in Chapter VI

$$p = (1 - \zeta)(1 - \zeta^2) \cdots (1 - \zeta^{p-1}),$$

so that

$$[p] = [1 - \zeta][1 - \zeta^2] \cdots [1 - \zeta^{p-1}].$$

Obviously $(1 - \zeta) \mid (1 - \zeta^j)$ for $j > 0$. Now choose t so that $jt \equiv 1 \pmod{p}$ Then

$$1 - \zeta = 1 - \zeta^{jt} = (1 - \zeta^j)(1 + \zeta^j + \cdots),$$

so $(1 - \zeta^j) \mid (1 - \zeta)$. Hence $1 - \zeta$ and $1 - \zeta^j$ are associates, so that $[1 - \zeta] = [1 - \zeta^j]$. Thus

$$[p] = [1 - \zeta]^{p-1} = L^{p-1}.$$

Since $(K/R) = p - 1$, $N[p] = |Np| = p^{p-1}$. Then $(NL)^{p-1} = p^{p-1}$, $NL = p$. By Corollary 9.15, L is a prime ideal.

LEMMA 10.7. *The number i is not in K, nor is the number $e^{2\pi i/q}$ if q is a prime different from p and greater than 2.*

Suppose i is in K. Since it is a unit $[1 + i] = [1 - i]$. Then

$$[2] = [1 + i][1 - i] = [1 + i]^2.$$

Since $2 \neq p$ this contradicts Corollary 9.7.

If $e^{2\pi i/q}$ is in K then, by the same argument used to prove Lemma 10.6,

$$[q] = [1 - e^{2\pi i/q}]^{q-1}.$$

Since $q > 2$, $[q]$ is ramified, again in contradiction to Corollary 9.7.

A root of unity α is a number such that $\alpha^m = 1$ for some positive integer m. Obviously α is of the form $e^{2\pi i t/m}$ where t is a rational integer.

LEMMA 10.8. *The only roots of unity in K are* $\pm \zeta^s$, $0 < s \leq p$.

Suppose $\alpha = e^{2\pi i t/m}$ is in K. We can assume that $m > 0$, $(m, t) = 1$. The lemma asserts that $m \mid 2p$. If $m \nmid 2p$ then one of the following must be true:

$$4 \mid m, \qquad q \mid m, \qquad \text{or} \quad p^2 \mid m,$$

where q is an odd prime different from p.

Since $(m, t) = 1$ we can find r so that $tr \equiv 1 \pmod{m}$, $tr = 1 + km$. Then

$$\alpha^r = e^{2\pi i tr/m} = e^{2\pi i (k+1/m)} = e^{2\pi i/m}$$

is in K.

If $4 \mid m$ then $e^{2\pi i/4} = i$ is in K, contradicting Lemma 10.7. If $q \mid m$ then $e^{2\pi i/q}$ is in K, also contradicting that lemma.

If $p^2 \mid m$ then $\tau = e^{2\pi i/p^2}$ is in K. We show that this is impossible. τ satisfies the equation $x^{p^2} - 1 = 0$, but not $x^p - 1 = 0$. Hence τ is a root of

$$\frac{x^{p^2} - 1}{x^p - 1} = x^{p(p-1)} + x^{p(p-2)} + \cdots + 1.$$

By Theorem 3.9, τ is of degree $p(p - 1) > p - 1$ over R, hence (Corollary 5.8) it cannot belong to K which is of degree $p - 1$ over R.

LEMMA 10.9. *For each integer α in K there is a rational integer a such that*

$$\alpha^p \equiv a \pmod{L^p}.$$

Since $NL = p$, there are p incongruent residue classes modulo L and, as we saw earlier, $0, 1, \cdots, p - 1$ form a complete residue system modulo L. Hence for a suitable rational integer b, $\alpha \equiv b \ (L)$. Now

$$\alpha^p - b^p = \prod_{m=0}^{p-1} (\alpha - \zeta^m b).$$

Since $\lambda = 1 - \zeta, \zeta \equiv 1(L)$ and each of the factors

$$\alpha - \zeta^m b \equiv \alpha - b \equiv 0 \ (L).$$

Hence $\alpha^p - b^p \equiv 0 \ (L^p)$.

LEMMA 10.10. *If all the coefficients of a monic polynomial are rational integers and all the roots are of absolute value 1 then these roots are roots of unity.*

Let the roots be $\omega_1, \cdots, \omega_k$. By the theorem on symmetric functions the polynomial

$$p_l(x) = (x - \omega_1^l)(x - \omega_2^l) \cdots (x - \omega_k^l)$$

is a monic polynomial with rational integral coefficients, for each fixed rational integer $l > 0$. Let

$$p_l(x) = x^k + a_{l,k-1}x^{k-1} + \cdots + a_{l,0}, \quad l = 1, 2, \cdots$$

denote these polynomials. Each a_{ij} is an elementary symmetric function in the roots $\omega_1, \cdots, \omega_k$; since these roots are of absolute value 1

$$| a_{lt} | \leq \binom{k}{t}.$$

Now $\binom{k}{t}$ is independent of l, so there can be only a finite number of different polynomials $p_l(x)$. So ω_i^l must be the same for two distinct values of l, say l_1 and l_2, where $l_1 > l_2$. Then $\omega_i^{l_1} = \omega_i^{l_2}$, $\omega_i^{l_1-l_2} = 1$, so that ω_i is a root of unity.

LEMMA 10.11. *Let ϵ be a unit in $R(\zeta)$. Then $\epsilon = \zeta^g r$, where g is a positive rational integer and r is a real number.*

Since 1, ζ, $\cdots$, ζ^{p-2} is an integral basis, $\epsilon = r(\zeta)$, where $r(\zeta)$ is a polynomial in ζ with rational integral coefficients. For $s = 1, \cdots, p - 1$ the number $\epsilon_s = r(\zeta^s)$ is conjugate to ϵ. Since $N\epsilon = \epsilon_1 \cdots \epsilon_{p-1} = \pm 1$, $\epsilon_s \mid 1$, so that each ϵ_s is a unit. Moreover,

$$\epsilon_{p-s} = r(\zeta^{p-s}) = r(\zeta^{-s}) = \overline{r(\zeta^s)},$$

where the bar denotes the complex-conjugate. Hence $\epsilon_{p-s} = \bar{\epsilon}_s$, $\epsilon_s \epsilon_{p-s} = \mid \epsilon_s \mid^2 > 0$. There are $p - 1$ of the ϵ_s; multiplying them in pairs we get $N\epsilon = \Pi \epsilon_s \epsilon_{p-s} > 0$, so that $N\epsilon = 1$.

The numbers $\epsilon_s/\epsilon_{p-s}$, $s = 1, \cdots, p - 1$, are units of absolute value 1. By the usual argument on symmetric functions the polynomial

$$\prod_{s=1}^{p-1} \left(x - \frac{\epsilon_s}{\epsilon_{p-s}} \right) = \prod_{s=1}^{p-1} (\epsilon_{p-s} \, x - \epsilon_s)$$

has rational integral coefficients. We conclude from Lemma 10.10 that $\epsilon_s/\epsilon_{p-s}$ is a root of unity. In particular if we let $s = 1$, we find that ϵ/ϵ_{p-1} is a root of unity. By Lemma 10.8, $\epsilon/\epsilon_{p-1} = \pm\zeta^t = \pm\zeta^{t+p}$. Since p is odd one of t or $t + p$ is even, so that $\dfrac{\epsilon}{\epsilon_{p-1}} = \pm\zeta^{2g}$, where g is a positive rational integer.

Modulo L the numbers $0, 1, \cdots, p - 1$ form a complete residue system. Hence for some one of them, v,

$$(10.4) \qquad \zeta^{-g}\epsilon \equiv v \ (L)$$

But $L = [\lambda]$, so that $\mu = \dfrac{\zeta^{-g}\epsilon - v}{\lambda}$ is an integer in K. Its complex-conjugate $\bar{\mu}$ is also an integer in K for both satisfy the same minimal polynomial. Then

$$\bar{\mu} = \frac{\bar{\zeta}^{-g}\bar{\epsilon} - v}{\bar{\lambda}} = \frac{\zeta^{g}\epsilon_{p-1} - v}{\bar{\lambda}}$$

is an integer. But $\bar{\lambda} = 1 - \zeta^{p-1}$ is an associate of λ (see the proof of Lemma 10.6). Hence $\dfrac{\zeta^{g}\epsilon_{p-1} - v}{\lambda}$ is also an integer. Then

$$\zeta^{g}\epsilon_{p-1} \equiv v \equiv \zeta^{-g}\epsilon \ (L)$$

by (10.4). This shows that $\dfrac{\epsilon}{\epsilon_{p-1}} \equiv \zeta^{2g} \ (L)$.

We can now decide for which choice of sign our previous conclusion $\dfrac{\epsilon}{\epsilon_{p-1}} = \pm\zeta^{2g}$ is correct. If the $-$ sign holds then $-\zeta^{2g} \equiv \zeta^{2g} \ (L)$, so that $L \mid 2\zeta^{2g}$, $NL \mid 2^{p-1}$, which contradicts Lemma 10.6. This means that $\epsilon = \zeta^{2g}\epsilon_{p-1}$, $\epsilon\zeta^{-g} = \epsilon_{p-1}\zeta^{g}$. Since the right- and left-hand sides of this equation are complex-conjugates and equal, they must be real. The lemma is established.

We are now in a position to prove the following simplified form of Kummer's theorem:

THEOREM 10.12. *If p is a regular odd prime, then*

$$(10.5) \qquad x^{p} + y^{p} + z^{p} = 0$$

has no solution in rational integers for which

$$p \nmid x, \qquad p \nmid y, \qquad p \nmid z.$$

We shall assume that the equation has a solution for which p does not divide any of h, x, y, z and arrive at a contradiction. If x and y have a common factor it is shared by z, and we can remove it by division. This justifies the assumption that x, y, and z have no common factor. From (10.5) we obtain

$$(10.6) \qquad \prod_{m=0}^{p-1} (x + \zeta^m y) = - z^p,$$

and then

$$(10.7) \qquad \prod_{m=0}^{p-1} [x + \zeta^m y] = [z]^p.$$

(Note the change in notation, signifying the passage from numbers to ideals.)

Each two of the ideals on the left of (10.7) are relatively prime. To prove this suppose P is a prime factor of both $[x + \zeta^k y]$ and $[x + \zeta^l y]$, $0 \le k < l \le p - 1$. Then P contains both $x + \zeta^k y$ and $x + \zeta^l y$, and hence their difference $y\zeta^k(1 - \zeta^{l-k})$. Since $1 - \zeta^{l-k}$ is an associate of $1 - \zeta = \lambda$ and ζ^k is a unit, P contains the number $y\lambda$. Hence P contains either y or λ, $P \mid y$ or $P \mid \lambda$. In addition, by (10.7) $P \mid z$, so P contains z and therefore P contains $z^p = x^p + y^p$. There are now two possibilities. (i) If P contains y it contains $x^p = z^p - y^p$, so $P \mid x$, $P \mid y$, contrary to the fact that x and y are relatively prime. (ii) If $P \mid \lambda$ then $P \mid L$. But L is prime, so that $P = L$. Then L contains z, $L \mid z$, $NL \mid Nz$, $p \mid z^{p-1}$, $p \mid z$, contrary to the hypothesis that $p \nmid z$. This proves the assertion made at the beginning of the paragraph.

We return to (10.7). Since the factors on the left-hand side are relatively prime, it follows from the fundamental theorem of ideal theory that each of them must be the pth power of an ideal. In particular $[x + \zeta y] = A^p$. Then A^p is principal, $A^p \sim (1)$ and, by Corollary 10.4, $A \sim (1)$. Hence A is itself a principal ideal (δ), and $[x + \zeta y] = [\delta]^p = [\delta^p]$. This shows that $x + \zeta y = \epsilon \delta^p$, where ϵ is a unit.

This step we have just taken is the decisive one. But could we not have drawn the same conclusion directly from (10.6) without the excursion into ideal theory? The answer is that without ideal theory we could have made the direct step only in the case when the field $R(\zeta)$ has class number 1—that is, when factorization of *integers* into primes is unique. Unfortunately there are cyclotomic fields of class number greater than 1.

Since $x + \zeta y = \epsilon \delta^p$ we can invoke Lemma 10.11 to conclude that $x + \zeta y = \zeta^g r \delta^p$, where r is a real number. According to Lemma 10.9, $\delta^p \equiv a(L^p)$ for some rational integer a. Hence $x + \zeta y \equiv \zeta^g r a \ (L^p)$. But (Lemma 10.6) $[p] \mid L^p$, and therefore $x + \zeta y \equiv \zeta^g r a \pmod{[p]}$. Since ζ^{-g} is a unit $\zeta^{-g}(x + \zeta y) \equiv r a$. Also $r a$ is a real, so that by taking complex-conjugates we find that $\zeta^g(x + \zeta^{-1} y) \equiv r a$. Combining the last two congruences yields

$$(10.8) \quad x\zeta^{-g} + y\zeta^{1-g} - x\zeta^g - y\zeta^{g-1} \equiv 0 \pmod{[p]}.$$

We digress for a moment to show that $1 + \zeta$ is a unit. Since

$$x^{p-1} + \cdots + 1 = (x - \zeta)(x - \zeta^2) \cdots (x - \zeta^{p-1}),$$

we find, on letting $x = -1$, that $(1 + \zeta) \mid 1$, establishing the assertion.

Observe next that $g \not\equiv 0 \pmod{p}$. For otherwise $\zeta^g = 1$ and (10.8) becomes $y(\zeta - \zeta^{-1}) \equiv 0$, $y(1 + \zeta)(1 - \zeta) \equiv 0$; then because $1 + \zeta$ is a unit $y(1 - \zeta) \equiv 0$, or $p \mid y\lambda$. Since $[p] = [\lambda]^{p-1}$, $p > 2$, $\lambda^2 \mid y\lambda$, $\lambda \mid y$, $N\lambda \mid Ny$, $p \mid y^{p-1}$, contrary to the hypothesis $p \nmid y$. Similarly $g \not\equiv 1 \pmod{p}$. For otherwise (10.8) becomes $x(\zeta^{-1} - \zeta) \equiv 0$, and a similar argument applies.

(10.8) can be then written

$$(10.9) \qquad \alpha p = x\zeta^{-g} + y\zeta^{1-g} - x\zeta^{g} - y\zeta^{g-1},$$

where α is an integer in K and none of the four exponents of ζ is divisible by p. The numbers $\zeta, \zeta^{2}, \cdots, \zeta^{p-1}$ form an integral basis for K, and the numbers $\zeta^{-g}, \zeta^{1-g}, \zeta^{g}, \zeta^{g-1}$ occur among them. Now

$$\alpha = \frac{x}{p}\zeta^{-g} + \frac{y}{p}\zeta^{1-g} - \frac{x}{p}\zeta^{g} - \frac{y}{p}\zeta^{g-1}.$$

If no two of the exponents are congruent modulo p then $p \mid x$ and $p \mid y$, for α is an integer and its representation in terms of the integral basis is unique and involves integral coefficients only. Since in fact $p \nmid x$, $p \nmid y$ by hypothesis, two of the exponents must be congruent modulo p. Since $g \not\equiv 0$, $g \not\equiv 1$, the only remaining possibility is $2g \equiv 1 \pmod{p}$.

Because $2g \equiv 1 \pmod{p}$, and $\zeta^{p} = 1$, (10.9) can be written

$$\alpha p \zeta^{g} = x + y\zeta - x\zeta^{2g} - y\zeta^{2g-1}$$
$$= (x - y)(1 - \zeta) = (x - y)\lambda.$$

Hence

$$N\alpha \cdot Np = N(x - y)N\lambda, \qquad N\alpha \cdot p^{p-1} = (x - y)^{p-1}p.$$

We conclude that $p \mid (x - y)$—that is, $x \equiv y \pmod{p}$.

If we go back to the very beginning and write (10.5) as

$$\prod_{m=0}^{p-1}(x + \zeta^{m}z) = -y^{p},$$

a similar argument shows that $x \equiv z \pmod{p}$. Hence

$$0 = x^{p} + y^{p} + z^{p} \equiv x^{p} + x^{p} + x^{p} \equiv 3x^{p} \pmod{p}.$$

Then $p \mid 3x^{p}$, but $p \nmid x$. Hence $p = 3$.

The only possible regular prime for which (10.5) has a solution is $p = 3$, and we shall rule out this case by showing that $x^3 + y^3 + z^3 = 0$ cannot have a solution in rational integers if $3 \nmid x$, $3 \nmid y$, $3 \nmid z$. Since -1, 0, 1 forms a complete residue system modulo 3 and $3 \nmid x$, $x \equiv \pm 1 \pmod 3$. Hence

$$x = 3k \pm 1, x^3 = 27k^3 \pm 27k^2 + 9k \pm 1,$$

so $x^3 \equiv \pm 1 \pmod 9$. Similarly $y^3 \equiv \pm 1$, $z^3 \equiv \pm 1 \pmod 9$, so that

$$0 = x^3 + y^3 + z^3 \equiv \pm 1 \pm 1 \pm 1 \pmod 9.$$

Obviously this can not be true for *any* choice of the $\pm$ signs. Theorem 10.12 is proved.

CHAPTER XI

MINKOWSKI'S LEMMA AND THE THEORY OF UNITS

1. **The Minkowski lemma.** We shall now introduce the famous "geometric" lemma of Minkowski which has important applications in number theory. In particular, it will yield a simple proof of Theorem 10.1, which at present stands unproved. In addition it will enable us to establish the basic theorem concerning the structure of the units in an algebraic number field.

THEOREM 11.1. *Let $\{a_{pq}\}$ be a set of n^2 real numbers, where $p, q = 1, 2, \cdots, n, n > 1$, and such that the determinant $\Delta = |a_{pq}|$ is not zero. Define the forms $L_p(u_1, \cdots, u_n)$ by*

$$L_p(u_1, \cdots, u_n) = \sum_{q=1}^{n} a_{pq} u_q, \qquad p = 1, \cdots, n$$

Let $k_1, \cdots, k_n$ be n positive numbers whose product is not less than $|\Delta|$. Then there exist rational integers $x_1, \cdots, x_n$ not all zero for which

$$(11.1) \quad \begin{aligned} |L_p(x_1, \cdots, x_n)| &< k_p, \qquad p = 1, \cdots, n-1, \\ |L_n(x_1, \cdots, x_n)| &\leq k_n. \end{aligned}$$

To see what this theorem means geometrically suppose for simplicity that $n = 2$ and that $|\Delta| = 1$. k_1 and k_2 are then any two positive numbers such that $k_1 k_2 \geq 1$. Let u_1 and u_2 represent the coordinates of a point (u_1, u_2) in the plane. Any equation of the form $|au_1 + bu_2| = c$ represents a pair of parallel lines. Hence the equations

$$|a_{11}u_1 + a_{12}u_2| = k_1$$
$$|a_{21}u_1 + a_{22}u_2| = k_2$$

represent two pairs of parallel lines. The four lines so represented are not parallel since $\Delta \neq 0$. It follows that these four lines bound a parallelogram. It is not difficult to show that the area of this parallelogram is $4k_1k_2$. Since $k_1k_2 \geq 1$ the area is at least 4. The theorem then says that a parallelogram with center at the origin and area at least 4 has the property that in it or on its boundary there is a point (u_1, u_2), different from $(0, 0)$ and different from a vertex, whose coordinates are both rational integers. The number 4 cannot be decreased, as the square bounded by the four lines $u_1 = \pm1$, $u_2 = \pm1$ shows. There is a corresponding interpretation of the general theorem for n dimensions, when "parallelogram" is replaced by "parallelotope" and the number 4 by 2^n.

We proceed to a proof of the theorem. A point $(x_1, \cdots, x_n)$ in n-dimensional space whose coordinates are all rational integers, but not all zero (note this last restriction!) we shall call a *lattice point*. The theorem states that there is at least one lattice point satisfying the conditions (11.1)

Suppose there is no such point. Then each lattice point satisfies at least one of the inequalities

$$|L_p(x_1, \cdots, x_n)| \geq k_p, \qquad p = 1, 2, \cdots, n - 1,$$
$$|L_n(x_1, \cdots, x_n)| > k_n.$$

Consider all those lattice points (if any exist) for which

$$|L_n(x_1, \cdots, x_n)| > k_n,$$

but for which

$$|L_p(x_1, \cdots, x_n)| < k_p, \qquad p = 1, 2, \cdots, n - 1.$$

For a sufficiently small positive ϵ they satisfy the inequality

$$|L_n(x_1, \cdots, x_n)| \geq k_n + \epsilon.$$

It follows that each lattice point satisfies at least one of the inequalities

$$(11.2) \quad \begin{aligned} &| L_p(x_1, \cdots, x_n) | \geq k_p, \qquad p = 1, \cdots, n - 1, \\ &| L_n(x_1, \cdots, x_n) | \geq k_n + \epsilon. \end{aligned}$$

From this we shall derive a contradiction.

Let $k'_p = k_p$, $p \neq n$, and $k'_n = k_n + \epsilon$. Now consider the region interior to the parallelotope P_0 defined by

$$(11.3) \qquad | L_p(u_1, \cdots, u_n) | < \frac{k'_p}{2}, \qquad p = 1, \cdots, n.$$

Let $g_1, \cdots, g_n$ be any lattice point. We can imagine P_0 translated so that $(0, \cdots, 0)$ becomes $(g_1, \cdots, g_n)$ and P_0 becomes the new figure $P_0(g_1, \cdots, g_n)$ defined by

$$| L_p(u_1 - g_1, \cdots, u_n - g_n) | < \frac{k'_p}{2}, \qquad p = 1, \cdots, n.$$

By varying $(g_1, \cdots, g_n)$ we obtain in this fashion an infinite number of such $P_0(g_1, \cdots, g_n)$ all geometrically congruent to the original one.

No two of these parallelotopes can have a point in common. For if both

$$| L_p(u_1 - g_1, \cdots, u_n - g_n) | < \frac{k'_p}{2}, \qquad p = 1, \cdots, n,$$

and

$$| L_p(u_1 - g'_1, \cdots, u_n - g'_n) | < \frac{k'_p}{2}, \qquad p = 1, \cdots, n$$

are true, where $(g_1, \cdots, g_n) \neq (g'_1, \cdots, g'_n)$, then

$$| L_p(g_1 - g'_1, \cdots, g_n - g'_n) | < k'_p, \qquad p = 1, \cdots, n,$$

contradicting the fact that one of the inequalities (11.2) holds for each lattice point.

Now let L be a positive integer, and consider the hypercube $|u_q| \leq L$, $q = 1, \cdots, n$. The sum of the volumes of all $P_0(g_1, \cdots, g_n)$ which lie in this cube is less than the volume $(2L)^n$ of the cube. Let c be the upper bound of the absolute values of the coordinates of all points in P_0. Then any $P_0(g_1, \cdots, g_n)$ belongs to the cube $|u_q| \leq L + c$ provided that $|g_q| \leq L, q = 1, \cdots, n$. There are $(2L + 1)^n - 1$ such $P_0(g_1, \cdots, g_n)$ exclusive of P_0, since each g_q satisfies $-L \leq g_q \leq L$. None of the $P_0(g_1, \cdots, g_n)$ overlap. Hence the cube $|u_q| \leq L + c$ contains parallelotopes of total volume $(2L + 1)^n J$, where J is the volume of one of them. The total volume of this cube is $(2L + 2c)^n$. Hence

$$J \leq \frac{(2L + 2c)^n}{(2L + 1)^n}.$$

Now let $L \to \infty$. It follows that $J \leq 1$; hence the volume of P_0 is at most 1.

We shall now compute the volume of P_0 by another method. According to (11.3) the volume of P_0 is given by the n-fold integral

$$J = \int_{|L_p| < k_p'/2} du_1 \cdots du_n.$$

Now make the change of variable $y_p = L_p(u_1, \cdots, u_n)$. The Jacobian of the transformation is just Δ, so that

$$J = \frac{1}{|\Delta|} \int_{|y_p| < k_p'/2} dy_1 \cdots dy_n = \frac{k_1' \cdots k_n'}{|\Delta|}.$$

But $k_1' \cdots k_n' = k_1 \cdots k_{n-1}(k_n + \epsilon) > k_1 \cdots k_n \geq |\Delta|$, according to the hypothesis of the theorem. Hence $J > 1$. This contradicts the preceding conclusion that $J \leq 1$. The assumption that no lattice point satisfies (11.1) must be retracted, and the theorem is established.

It is important to see what happens to the theorem

when the a_{pq} are permitted to be complex numbers. We shall show that with appropriate changes the theorem remains true even in this case.

Let L_p, $p = 1, \cdots, n$ be the forms defined as before by

$$\sum_{q=1}^{n} a_{pq}\, u_q, \qquad\qquad p = 1, \cdots, n,$$

but now permitting the a_{pq} to be complex. Number the L_p so that the first r_1, $0 \leq r_1 \leq n$, are real,* the remaining ones imaginary. It is assumed that the imaginary ones are even in number, say $2r_2$, and that with each one which appears on the list as L_p with $r_1 < p \leq r_2$, its complex-conjugate $\bar{L}_p$ also appears on the list, as L_{p+r_2}. The list now reads

$$\underbrace{L_1, \cdots, L_{r_1}}_{\text{real}}\; ; \; \underbrace{L_{r_1+1}, \cdots, L_{r_1+r_2}}_{\text{imaginary}}\; ; \; \underbrace{L_{r_1+1+r_2}, \cdots, L_{r_1+2r_2}}_{\text{complex-conjugates}}.$$

Obviously $n = r_1 + 2r_2$. As before, it will be supposed that $k_1, \cdots, k_n$ are positive numbers for which $k_1 k_2 \cdots k_n \geq |\Delta|$, and moreover that they have the property $k_{r_1+s} = k_{r_1+s+r_2}$, $s = 1, \cdots, r_2$. Thus the k_i corresponding to a pair of complex-conjugate forms are the same.

In order to apply our previous work we define a new set of forms L'_p as follows: let

$$L'_p = \begin{cases} L_p, \qquad p = 1, \cdots, r_1 \\[2mm] \dfrac{L_p + \bar{L}_p}{\sqrt{2}} = \dfrac{L_p + L_{p+r_2}}{\sqrt{2}}, \\[2mm] \qquad\qquad p = r_1 + 1, \cdots, r_1 + r_2 \\[2mm] \dfrac{L_p - \bar{L}_p}{\sqrt{2}\,i} = \dfrac{L_p - L_{p-r_2}}{\sqrt{2}\,i}, \\[2mm] \qquad\qquad p = r_1 + r_2 + 1, \cdots, r_1 + 2r_2. \end{cases}$$

* This means that none of the a_{pq} which appear are imaginary.

(If $r_1 = 0$ the list is understood to begin with the second group.) The set of forms L'_p is real, and its determinant has the same absolute value $|\Delta|$ as the original set of forms L_p(why?) This enables us to apply Theorem 11.1 to the L'_p. Before doing so let us choose any integer a, $1 \leq a \leq n$, and move L'_a to the end of the list of L'_p. It follows that a lattice-point $(x_1, \cdots, x_n)$ exists such that

$$(11.4) \quad \begin{aligned} |L'_p(x_1, \cdots, x_n)| &< k_p, \quad p = 1, \cdots, n, p \neq a, \\ |L'_a(x_1, \cdots, x_n)| &\leq k_a. \end{aligned}$$

In order to apply these inequalities to L_p, let us find L_p in terms of L'_p. Clearly

$$L_p = L'_p, \qquad p = 1, \cdots, r_1,$$

$$\left. \begin{aligned} L_p &= \frac{\sqrt{2}}{2}(L'_p - i\,L'_{p+r_2}) \\ L_{p+r_2} &= \overline{L}_p \end{aligned} \right\} \; p = r_1 + 1, \cdots r_1 + r_2.$$

Hence

$$|L_p| = |L_p|, \qquad p = 1, \cdots, r_1,$$

$$|L_p| = |L_{p+r_2}| = \frac{1}{\sqrt{2}} \{ |L'_p|^2 + |L'_{p+r_2}|^2 \}^{1/2},$$

$$p = r_1 + 1, \cdots, r_1 + r_2.$$

(If $r_1 = 0$ we ignore the first of these two displays.)

Now let a be any integer, $1 \leq a \leq r_1 + r_2$. It follows from the preceding formulas and the inequalities (11.4) that

$$|L_p(x_1, \cdots, x_n)| < k_p, \quad p = 1, \cdots, r_1 + r_2, p \neq a,$$
$$|L_a(x_1, \cdots, x_n)| \leq k_a.$$

Since $|L_p| = |L_{p+r_2}|$, $p = r_1 + 1, \cdots, r_1 + r_2$ we have proved

Corollary 11.2. *There exists a lattice point such that*

$$| L_p(x_1, \cdots, x_n) | \leq k_p, \qquad p = 1, \cdots, n.$$

Moreover, the inequality can be replaced by a strict one except for one real form L_a, or two complex-conjugate forms L_a, L_{a+r_2}, chosen in advance.

One particular case is of special interest. Suppose $n = 2$, $r_1 = 0$, $r_2 = 1$—that is, both forms are imaginary. In that case $k_1 = k_2$ and

$$| L_1 | = | L_2 | = \frac{1}{\sqrt{2}} \{ | L_1' |^2 + | L_2' |^2 \}^{1/2},$$

so that by (11.4) we can conclude that both $| L_1 |$ *and* $| L_2 |$ are less than k_1. This conclusion cannot be drawn directly from the corollary.

2. **Applications.** We are now in a position to prove Theorem 10.1. Let $\alpha_1, \cdots, \alpha_n$ be a basis for the ideal A and let $\alpha_i^{(j)}, j = 1, \cdots, n$ be the conjugates of α_i. Consider the forms $\sum_{i=1}^{n} \alpha_i^{(j)} u_i, j = 1, \cdots, n$. Their determinant $\{\Delta[\alpha_1, \cdots, \alpha_n]\}^{1/2} = NA \cdot | d |^{1/2} \neq 0$. We can apply Corollary 11.2 with all the k_p equal to $\{NA \cdot | d |^{1/2}\}^{1/n}$. This yields a lattice point $(x_1, \cdots, x_n)$ such that if $\omega_j = \sum_{i=1}^{n} \alpha_i^{(j)} x_i$, then

$$| \omega_j | \leq \{NA \cdot | d |^{1/2}\}^{1/n}, \quad j = 1, \cdots, n.$$

Moreover by the second part of the corollary and the remarks following it at least one of the inequalities can be replaced by a strict one. Hence

$$| N\omega | = | \omega_1 \cdots \omega_n | < NA \cdot | d |^{1/2}.$$

Another important consequence of the Minkowski theory is

Theorem 11.3. *The discriminant d of an algebraic number field different from R has the property $| d | > 1$.*

To prove this let A be the ideal (1). According to Theorem 10.1 there is an integer $\alpha \neq 0$ in (1) such that $|N\alpha| < N((1)) \cdot |d|^{1/2} = |d|^{1/2}$. Since $\alpha \neq 0$, $|N\alpha| \geq 1$. Hence $|d| > 1$.

It should be observed that the conclusion of Theorem 11.3 is false for the field R, for in this case $d = 1$. Note also that in this case the Minkowski lemma is not available, since it requires that $n > 1$.

In the following sections the theory will be used to study the units in a field. The proof of the fundamental theorem is in the main that outlined by Ore in his tract (see the bibliography). The reader will find it useful to review the elementary material on units given in Chapter VII.

3. The Dirichlet-Minkowski theorem on units.

As we saw earlier, all the units in the real quadratic field $R(\sqrt{2})$ are of the form $\pm(1 + \sqrt{2})^k$, $k = 0, \pm 1, \cdots$. It is our purpose to obtain a generalization of this theorem for other algebraic number fields.

Let $K = R(\theta)$ be of degree n over R and let $\theta_1, \cdots, \theta_n$ be the conjugates of θ. The θ_i all satisfy the same minimal polynomial $p(x)$. Since the coefficients of $p(x)$ are real, any imaginary root θ_i has paired with it a complex-conjugate root θ_j. Let r_1 be the number of real roots and $2r_2$ the number of imaginary roots, where $n = r_1 + 2r_2$. Number the roots so that $\theta_1, \cdots, \theta_r$, are real and θ_{r_1+1}, $\cdots, \theta_n$ are imaginary.* Arrange the numbering of the latter set so that θ_{r_1+t} and $\theta_{r_1+r_2+t}$, $t = 1, \cdots, r_2$, are complex-conjugates. Finally, let $r = r_1 + r_2 - 1$.

If $r = 0$ the structure of the units in K is easily settled. For then $r_1 + r_2 = 1$, so $r_2 = 0$ or 1; since $n = 1 + r_2$,

---

* Observe that in order to do this we abandon our previous convention that $\theta_1 = \theta$.

$n = 1$ or 2. If $n = 1$ the field is R; if $n = 2$, $r_2 = 1$ and the field is imaginary quadratic. The units in these cases have already been described in Chapter VII. In what follows we shall therefore assume that $r \geq 1$.

Observe that any root of unity ρ in K is a unit, for if $\rho^m = 1$, $N(\rho)^m = 1$, so $N(\rho) = \pm 1$. The number of roots of unity in K is finite, for the degree of any one of them must divide n and there are only a finite number of roots of unity of each degree.

If $\epsilon_1, \cdots, \epsilon_t$ are units in K, so are all numbers of the form $\epsilon = \rho \epsilon_1^{a_1} \cdots \epsilon_t^{a_t}$, where the a_i are rational integers and ρ is a root of unity. This follows from the fact that the product of units is a unit. The t units $\epsilon_1, \cdots, \epsilon_t$ are *independent* if there is no relation of the form

$$(11.5) \qquad \epsilon_1^{a_1} \cdots \epsilon_t^{a_t} = 1$$

with the a_i rational integers unless all the a_i vanish. If there is such a relation and $t > 1$, each ϵ_i is said to *depend* on the others. Observe that if $\epsilon_1, \cdots, \epsilon_t$ are independent then no relation of the form

$$\epsilon_1^{b_1} \cdots \epsilon_t^{b_t} = \rho$$

can hold with the b_i rational numbers. For by raising each side to a sufficiently high power we can bring it into the form (11.5).

The principal theorem on the structure of the units of K is the following.

THEOREM 11.4. *If $r \geq 1$, then there exist r independent units $\xi_1, \cdots, \xi_r$ in K such that every unit η can be expressed uniquely in the form*

$$\eta = \rho \xi_1^{a_1} \cdots \xi_r^{a_r},$$

where the a_i are rational integers and ρ is a root of unity in K.

The proof will proceed in three parts. First we prove

the existence of r independent units $\epsilon_1, \cdots, \epsilon_r$. Secondly we prove that there exist r independent units $\xi_1, \cdots, \xi_r$ such that any unit which depends on $\epsilon_1, \cdots, \epsilon_r$ can be expressed uniquely in the form prescribed by the theorem. Finally we prove that each $r + 1$ units in K are dependent, so that *all* units depend on $\epsilon_1, \cdots, \epsilon_r$.

Each of these three steps will be discussed in a separate section.

4. The existence of r independent units.

According to the proof of Theorem 11.3 there is an integer $\lambda \neq 0$ in K such that $|N\lambda| < |d|^{1/2}$. Let us consider all λ with this property. Each determines an ideal (λ), of norm equal to $|N\lambda|$. But there are at most a finite number of ideals of given norm, and hence only a finite number of ideals $(\lambda_1), \cdots, (\lambda_s)$ of norm less than $|d|^{1/2}$. It follows that any λ for which $|N\lambda| < |d|^{1/2}$ is associated with one of the numbers $\lambda_1, \cdots, \lambda_s$. Let $\lambda_j^{(i)}$ denote the conjugates of λ_j, and l the smallest of the numbers $|\lambda_j^{(i)}|, j = 1, \cdots, s, i = 1, \cdots, n$.

Let $\alpha_1, \cdots, \alpha_n$ be an integral basis for K. We are going to apply Corollary 11.2 to the forms

$$\sum_{j=1}^{n} \alpha_j^{(i)} u_j, \qquad i = 1, \cdots, n.$$

The determinant is $|d|^{1/2}$. The reader is reminded of the convention established in § 3 concerning the numbering of conjugates. It follows that the first r_1 of the preceding forms are real, the remaining ones falling into pairs of complex-conjugates.* Let a be a rational integer $1 \leq a \leq r_1 + r_2$. If a corresponds to a real form let $k_i = l$ except

* If any of the remaining forms were real, two would be the same, so that $\Delta[\alpha_1 \cdots \alpha_n] = 0$, contradicting the fact that $\alpha_1, \cdots, \alpha_n$ is a basis.

for $i = a$, and if a corresponds to an imaginary form let $k_i = l$ except for $i = a$, $i = a + r_2$. Choose the remaining k_i so that the product of all the k_i is $|d|^{1/2}$, and so that $k_a = k_{a+r_2}$ in the second of the two cases. According to Corollary 11.2 we can find rational integers $x_1, \cdots, x_n$ not all zero so that

$$\left| \sum_{j=1}^{n} \alpha_j^{(i)} x_j \right| < l,$$

for all i except $i = a$ in the first case, and except $i = a$, $i = a + r_2$ in the second. Let μ_a denote the integer $\sum_{j=1}^{n} \alpha_j x_j$. Then

$$| N(\mu_a) | = | \mu_a^{(1)} | \cdots | \mu_a^{(n)} | < k_1 \cdots k_n = | d |^{1/2}.$$

According to the preceding paragraph μ_a is associated with one of the numbers λ_j, so $\mu_a = \epsilon_a \lambda_j$, where ϵ_a is a unit. Now $| \mu_a^{(i)} | < l, i = 1, \cdots, r_1 + r_2, i \neq a$. Hence

$$| \epsilon_a^{(i)} | = | \mu_a^{(i)} | | \lambda_j^{(i)} |^{-1} < l \cdot \frac{1}{l} = 1$$

for $i = 1, \cdots, r_1 + r_2, i \neq a$. Now $| N\epsilon_a | = | \epsilon_a^{(1)} | \cdots | \epsilon_a^{(n)} | = 1$. Moreover, according to the numbering of the conjugates each of the factors except $\epsilon_a^{(a)}$, and its complex-conjugate if it occurs, is less than 1 in absolute value. Hence $| \epsilon_a^{(a)} | > 1$.

Since $1 \leq a < r_1 + r_2$, a can take on the $r + 1$ values $1, 2, \cdots, r + 1$. We have therefore found $r + 1$ units $\epsilon_1, \cdots, \epsilon_{r+1}$ such that for $i = 1, \cdots, r + 1$

(11.6) $| \epsilon_j^{(i)} | < 1, i \neq j; \qquad | \epsilon_i^{(i)} | > 1.$

It will now be shown that $\epsilon_1, \cdots, \epsilon_r$ are independent. For suppose that $\epsilon_1^{a_1} \cdots \epsilon_r^{a_r} = 1$. Since the a_i are rational integers

$$a_1 \log | \epsilon_1^{(i)} | + \cdots + a_r \log | \epsilon_r^{(i)} | = 0, \quad i = 1, \cdots, r.$$

We shall show that all the a_i must be zero. If they are not then the determinant $|l_{ij}|$ vanishes, $l_{ij} = \log|\epsilon_j^{(i)}|$, $i = 1, \cdots, r; j = 1, \cdots, r$. Let $e_i = 1, i = 1, \cdots, r_1$; $e_i = 2, i = r_1 + 1, \cdots, r$. Then the determinant $|e_i l_{ij}|$ also vanishes, since we have only multiplied each row by a constant. The equations

$$\sum_{i=1}^{r} x_i e_i l_{ij} = 0, \qquad j = 1, \cdots, r,$$

therefore have a non-trivial solution $x_1, \cdots, x_r$. Choose that x_i which has the largest absolute value; we may suppose it to be x_1. The first of the equations is

$$-x_1 e_1 l_{11} = x_2 e_2 l_{21} + \cdots + x_r e_r l_{r1},$$

and so

$$|x_1||e_1||l_{11}| \le |x_1|(e_2|l_{21}| + \cdots + e_r|l_{r1}|).$$

By (11.6), $l_{11} > 0$, $l_{i1} < 0$, $i = 2, \cdots, r$. Hence

$$e_1 l_{11} \le -e_2 l_{21} - \cdots - e_r l_{r1},$$

so that

$$(11.7) \qquad e_1 l_{11} + e_2 l_{21} + \cdots + e_r l_{r1} \le 0.$$

From this we can obtain a contradiction.

Since

$$N(\epsilon_1) = \epsilon_1^{(1)} \cdots \epsilon_1^{(n)} = 1,$$
$$\log|\epsilon_1^{(1)}| + \cdots + \log|\epsilon_1^{(n)}| = 0.$$

According to the numbering of the conjugates $|\epsilon_1^{(k)}| = |\epsilon_1^{(k+r_2)}|$, $k > r_1$. Hence

$$\sum_{i=1}^{r_1+r_2} e_i \log|\epsilon_1^{(i)}| = 0.$$

But this sum is

$$e_1 l_{11} + e_2 l_{21} + \cdots + e_r l_{r1} + e_{r_1+r_2} \log|\epsilon_1^{(r+1)}|.$$

By (11.6) the last term is negative, so the sum of the first r terms is positive, contrary to (11.7). So our assumption that $\epsilon_1, \cdots, \epsilon_r$ are dependent was erroneous.

We have proved incidentally that the determinant $| \log | \epsilon_j^{(i)} | |$, $i = 1, \cdots, r, j = 1, \cdots, r$, does not vanish.

5. **The second part of the proof.** Let $\epsilon_1, \cdots, \epsilon_r$ be the units obtained in the preceding section. We wish to prove the existence of independent units $\xi_1, \cdots, \xi_r$ such that each unit η depending on $\epsilon_1, \cdots, \epsilon_r$ has the form $\eta = \rho \xi_1^{a_1} \cdots \xi_r^{a_r}$ where the a_i are rational integers and ρ is a root of unity in K. The uniqueness of this representation follows from the independence of the ξ_i.

LEMMA 11.5. *There is a positive number A such that if the absolute value $| \omega^{(i)} |$ of each of the conjugates of an integer ω is less than $1 + A$, then ω is a root of unity.*

There are only a finite number of integers α in K such that all its conjugates are less than 2 in absolute value. For let

$$(x - \alpha^{(1)}) \cdots (x - \alpha^{(n)}) = x^n + a_{n-1}x^{n-1} + \cdots + a_0$$

be the field polynomial for α. Since each a_i is an elementary symmetric function in the roots, and since each root is in absolute value less than 2, we have

$$| a_i | \leq \binom{n}{i} 2^{n-i}.$$

The a_i are rational integers, and therefore can take on only a finite number of different values. There are then only a finite number of different polynomials for integers of the prescribed kind, and so only a finite number N of such integers.

Choose A so that $A > 0$, $(1 + A)^{N+1} < 2$. This A has the desired property, as we now prove. Suppose ω is an integer such that $|\omega^{(i)}| < 1 + A$, $i = 1, \cdots, n$. The absolute values of the conjugates of the integers ω^k, $k = 1, \cdots, N+1$, are all less than $(1 + A)^k \leq (1 + A)^{N+1} < 2$, so that there must be two exponents k', k, $k' > k$, such that $\omega^{k'} = \omega^k$. Then $\omega^{k'-k} = 1$, and ω is a root of unity. The lemma is established.

Suppose η depends on the units $\epsilon_1, \cdots, \epsilon_r$. For some rational integer N

$$\eta^N \epsilon_1^{a_1} \cdots \epsilon_r^{a_r} = 1, \qquad \eta = \rho\epsilon_1^{-a_1/N} \cdots \epsilon_t^{-a_r/N},$$

where ρ is in K, $\rho^N = 1$, and the a_i are rational integers. Then η and its conjugates are of the form

$$(11.8) \qquad \eta^{(i)} = \rho^{(i)}\epsilon_1^{(i)s_1} \cdots \epsilon_r^{(i)s_r}, \quad i = 1, \cdots, n,$$

where $\rho^{(i)}$ is an Nth root of unity and the s_j are rational numbers.

Now consider the expression

$$\sigma = \eta^y \epsilon_1^{-x_1} \cdots \epsilon_r^{-x_r}.$$

We wish to show that for suitable choice of $y, x_1, \cdots, x_r$ as rational integers, σ is a root of unity. By (11.8)

$$(11.9) \qquad |\sigma^{(i)}| = |\epsilon_1^{(i)}|^{ys_1-x_1} \cdots |\epsilon_r^{(i)}|^{ys_r-x_r}.$$

The $r + 1$ linear forms $L_i(y, x_1, \cdots, x_r)$, where

$$L_1 = ys_1 - x_1, \cdots, L_r = ys_r - x_r, L_{r+1} = y,$$

has determinant of absolute value 1. By Theorem 11.1 we can find for each δ, $0 < \delta < 1$, a set of rational integers $y, x_1, \cdots, x_r$ not all zero such that

$$|ys_1 - x_1| < \delta, \cdots, |ys_r - x_r| < \delta, |y| \leq \delta^{-r},$$

(11.9) becomes

$$|\sigma^{(i)}| < |\epsilon_1^{(i)} \cdots \epsilon_r^{(i)}|^\delta.$$

Choose δ so small that $|\sigma^{(i)}| < 1 + A$. By Lemma 11.5 σ is a root of unity. From the definition of σ it follows that η can be written in the form

$$\eta = \sigma^{1/y} \epsilon_1^{x_1/y} \cdots \epsilon_r^{x_r/y}.$$

Observe that δ depends only on $\epsilon_1, \cdots, \epsilon_r$ and that $|y|$ is less than a bound depending only on $\epsilon_1, \cdots, \epsilon_r$. Hence *any unit η depending on $\epsilon_1, \cdots, \epsilon_r$ can be written in the form*

$$(11.10) \qquad \eta = \sigma^{x_0/M} \epsilon_1^{x_1/M} \cdots \epsilon_r^{x_r/M},$$

where σ is a root of unity and M is a positive integer depending only on the ϵ_i. This representation is unique, for the ϵ_i are independent.

Not all numbers of the form (11.10) belong to the field K for arbitrary rational integers x_i. But consider all units in K expressible in that form; an example is $\epsilon_i^{M/M}$. For each i, $i = 1, \cdots, r$, choose one such unit,

$$\xi_i = \sigma^{x_{0i}/M} \epsilon_1^{x_{1i}/M} \cdots \epsilon_i^{x_{ii}/M} \cdots \epsilon_r^{x_{ri}/M}$$

for which $x_{ii} > 0$ is least.

The ξ_i so chosen have the property specified at the beginning of this section. For let η be a unit dependent on $\epsilon_1, \cdots, \epsilon_r$; it is necessarily of the form (11.10). By Theorem 1.1,

$$x_r = a_r x_{rr} + t_r, \qquad 0 \le t_r < x_{rr},$$

so that

$$\eta \xi_r^{-a_r} = \sigma^{x'_0/M} \epsilon_1^{x'_1/M} \cdots \epsilon_{r-1}^{x'_{r-1}/M} \epsilon_r^{t_r/M},$$

for suitable integers x'_i. η and ξ_r are dependent on $\epsilon_1, \cdots, \epsilon_r$ so $\eta \xi_r^{-a_r}$ is also. Since $0 \le t_r < x_{rr}$ and x_{rr} is a minimum, $t_r = 0$ and

$$\eta \xi_r^{-a_r} = \sigma^{x'_0/M} \epsilon_1^{x'_1/M} \cdots \epsilon_{r-1}^{x'_{r-1}/M}.$$

Now repeat the procedure with x'_{r-1}, $\cdots$. Eventually we obtain

$$\eta \xi_r^{-a_r} \xi_{r-1}^{-a_{r-1}} \cdots \xi_1^{-a_1} = \sigma^{x/M},$$

where $\rho = \sigma^{x/M}$ is a root of unity in the field. Then $\eta = \rho \xi_1^{a_1} \cdots \xi_r^{a_r}$ is of the desired form.

To show the uniqueness of this representation we need only show that ξ_1, $\cdots$, ξ_r are independent. Write

$$\epsilon_j = \rho_j \xi_1^{b_{1j}} \xi_2^{b_{2j}} \cdots \xi_r^{b_{rj}}.$$

Since $|\rho_i| = 1$ we have

$$\log |\epsilon_j^{(i)}| = b_{1j} \log |\xi_1^{(i)}| + b_{2j} \log |\xi_2^{(i)}| \\ + \cdots + b_{rj} \log |\xi_r^{(i)}|,$$

$i, j = 1, \cdots, r$. If the ξ_j are not independent then the determinant $|\log |\xi_j^{(i)}||$ vanishes, by the argument used in the preceding section. Then the determinant

$$|\log |\epsilon_j^{(i)}|| = |b_{ij}||\log |\xi_j^{(i)}|| = 0,$$

contradicting the fact that $|\log |\epsilon_j^{(i)}|| \neq 0$.

6. **The proof completed.** It remains only to show that *any* $r + 1$ units ϵ_0, ϵ_1, $\cdots$, ϵ_r are dependent. The r equations

$$(11.11) \qquad \sum_{j=0}^{r} c_j \log |\epsilon_j^{(i)}| = 0, \qquad i = 1, \cdots, r,$$

in the $r + 1$ unknowns c_j have a solution for real c_j not all zero. Hence

$$(11.12) \qquad |\epsilon_0^{(i)}|^{c_0} \cdots |\epsilon_r^{(i)}|^{c_r} = 1, \quad i = 1, \cdots, r.$$

As we showed at the end of §4, any unit ϵ_j has the property

$$e_{r+1} \log |\epsilon_j^{(r+1)}| = -\sum_{i=1}^{r} e_i \log |\epsilon_j^{(i)}|.$$

Then multiplying each side by c_j and summing we obtain

$$e_{r+1} \sum_{j=0}^{r} c_j \log | \epsilon_j^{(r+1)} | = - \sum_{j=0}^{r} c_j \sum_{i=1}^{r} e_i \log | \epsilon_j^{(i)} |$$

$$= - \sum_{i=1}^{r} e_i \sum_{j=0}^{r} c_j \log | \epsilon_j^{(i)} | = 0,$$

by (11.11). Hence $\sum_{j=0}^{r} c_j \log | \epsilon_j^{(r+1)} | = 0$, so that (11.11) holds also for $i = r + 1$; it follows from the enumeration of the conjugates that (11.11), and hence (11.12), hold for $i = 1, \cdots, n$.

Not all the c_j are zero; we may suppose $c_0 \neq 0$. By (11.12)

$$| \epsilon_0^{(i)} | = | \epsilon_1^{(i)} |^{-c_1/c_0} \cdots | \epsilon_r^{(i)} |^{-c_r/c_0}, \qquad i = 1, \cdots, n.$$

By the same argument which took us from (11.8) to (11.10)

$$\epsilon_0 = \sigma^{x_0/M} \epsilon_1^{x_1/M} \cdots \epsilon_r^{x_r/M},$$

so that the units $\epsilon_0, \epsilon_1, \cdots, \epsilon_r$ are dependent.

REFERENCES

1. Birkhoff and MacLane, *Survey of Modern Algebra*, New York, 1948.
2. Hardy and Wright, *The Theory of Numbers*, Oxford, 1938.
3. E. Hecke, *Theorie der Algebraischen Zahlen*, Leipzig, 1923.
4. D. Hilbert, *Die Theorie der Algebraischen Zahlkörper*, No. 7 of Gesammelte Abhandlungen, Berlin, 1932.
5. E. Landau, *Einführung in die Elementare und Analytische Theorie der Algebraischen Zahlen und der Ideale*, Leipzig and Berlin, 1918.
6. E. Landau, *Vorlesungen über Zahlentheorie*, 3 volumes, Leipzig, 1927.
7. O. Ore, *Les Corps Algébriques et la Théorie des Idéaux*, Paris, 1934.
8. L. W. Reid, *The Elements of the Theory of Algebraic Numbers*, New York, 1910.
9. J. M. Thomas, *Theory of Equations*, New York, 1938.
10. H. S. Vandiver, *Fermat's Last Theorem*, American Mathematical Monthly, vol. 53 (1946), pp. 555-578.
11. Herman Weyl, *Algebraic Theory of Numbers*, Princeton, 1940.

INDEX

143

DATE DUE

GAYLORD			PRINTED IN U.S.A.